THIS BOOK BELONGS TO

WORKBOOK TO

A FUN HOMESCHOOLING HISTORY CURRICULUM FOR KIDS!

Ancient Civilizations of the World: Mesopotamia, Egypt, Greece, and Rome

By
The Insightful Scholar
Part of The Insightful Scholar
History Curriculum Series

MAAC Publishing

Written and Published in the USA

ISBN 979-8-9870786-3-1 (print)
ISBN 979-8-9870786-4-8 (ebook)

theinsightfulscholar.com

About This Book

The scope of this book focuses on Mesopotamia and the Mediterranean regions due to the volume of information covered. However, we explore other ancient civilizations around the world in other books.

Our reading book, workbook, and journal follow the same topics and are intended to complement each other. Students can also use the internet, library books, and videos to assist them in their research.

We provide several valuable additional free resources, which you can access at theinsghtfulscholar.com.

These resources include:

- Parent-Teacher Guide (includes answers to workbook questions)
- Bibliography with additional references
- Color images with citations
- Glossary
- Timeline

In addition, we will direct the students to an outside resource for some activities. Links can change or break, so we provide links in the Parent-Teacher Guide so they can be easily updated. We appreciate parents and teachers letting us know if a broken link is found.

This book was written for ages ten and up but can be used by younger children with help from the teacher!

CHILDREN SHOULD BE SUPERVISED WHEN CONDUCTING ACTIVITIES AND PROPER SAFETY PRECAUTIONS SHOULD BE TAKEN WHERE NEEDED.

This workbook covers:

- Critical Thinking
- Reading
- Creative Writing
- Problem Solving
- Math and Finance
- Vocabulary
- Research
- Drawing
- Arts and Crafts
- And More!

Table of Contents

Meet Pavi & Piper ... 6

Introduction ... 7
How Do We Know About History? ... 8
The Father of History ... 9
Oral Traditions ... 10
Crossword Puzzle ... 12
Storytelling ... 14
Grammar and Stories ... 16
Word Scramble ... 18
Name Your Price ... 19
Artifacts ... 20
The Ages of History ... 21
What's Different? ... 23
Introduction Quiz ... 24

Chapter 1 - Becoming Civilized ... 25
Our Stone Age Ancestors ... 27
Prehistoric Cave ... 28
Hunter-Gatherer Societies ... 29
The Ages of History ... 30
Word Search ... 31
Wonder While You Wander ... 32
Complete the Sentence ... 33
Copywork ... 34
Catal Huyuk ... 36
Tinker Tools ... 37
The Seven Wonders of the World ... 38
Chapter 1 Quiz ... 39

Chapter 2 - The Sumerians ... 40
Mesopotamian Rulers ... 43
Let's Bake! Cuneiform Writing ... 45
Crossword Puzzle ... 46
Identification Card ... 47
The Great Flood ... 48
Mesopotamian Home Life ... 49
Inventions and Achievements ... 50
What's Different? ... 51
Grammar & Stories ... 52
Building Big Ships ... 54
Scrapbook ... 57
Chapter 2 Quiz ... 58

Chapter 3 - The Babylonians ... 60
Babylonian Hanging Gardens ... 63
The Tower of Babel and Language ... 64
The Ishtar Gate ... 66
Authentic Babylonian Foods ... 67
Akitu Festival ... 68
The Code of Hammurabi ... 70
Word Search ... 71
Word Match ... 72
Copywork ... 73
Babel Budget ... 75
Time to Relax ... 78
Scrapbook ... 79
Chapter 3 Quiz ... 80

Chapter 4 - Egyptian Civilizations ... 81
Triangles ... 83
A Pyramid Tomb Floor Plan ... 84
What's Different? ... 85
Video of Egypt for Kids ... 86
Making Egyptian Paper ... 87
Writing Egyptian Hieroglyphics ... 88
Piles of Pyramids ... 90
Crossword Puzzle ... 91
Grammar & Stories ... 92
Scrapbook ... 94

Chapter 4 Quiz....95

Chapter 5 - Egyptian Time Periods....96
Hatshepsut....98
Frontalism....99
Egyptian Food....100
Curses on Tombs....101
King Tut Time Game....102
Mummified Apples....103
Egyptian Numbers....104
Copywork....106
Word Scramble....108
Time to Relax....109
Scrapbook....110
Chapter 5 Quiz....111

Chapter 6 - Other Mediterranean Civilizations....114
Authentic Mediterranean Recipes....116
Draw and Color....117
The Tyrians....118
The Minoans....119
The Mycenaeans....121
The Phoenicians....123
"Tyrian" Purple Tie Dye (sort of)....125
Grammar & Stories....126
The Minoan Double Axe....128
Word Search....129
Scrapbook....130
Chapter 6 Quiz....131

Chapter 7 - The Greeks....133
Greek Mythology....136
The Olympics....138
Draw and Color....140
Cooking Greek Cuisine....141
The Greek Chiton....142
Debate....143
Socrates....145
Family Tree....147
Copywork....149
Word Match....151
Scrapbook....153
Chapter 7 Quiz....154

Chapter 8 - The Romans....156
Marketing....159
Roman Emperors....160
Toga Time....161
Draw and Color....162
Cooking in Rome....163
Create A Newspaper For Ancient Rome....164
Build a Roman Road Model....165
Timeline Matchup....166
Grammar & Stories....167
Word Scramble....169
Roman Numerals....170
Scrapbook....171
Chapter 8 Quiz....172

Conclusion....174
Civilization Favorites....175
Compare and Contrast....177
Make Your Own Lyre....179
Ancient Religions....180
World Waterways....181
Forms of Currency....183
Forms of Government....185
What's Different?....187
Scrapbook....188
Conclusion Questions of What You Have Learned....189

Meet Pavi & Piper

Hi! I'm Pavi, and I'm Piper! And we are two lifelong friends who want to take you on a very fun learning adventure! Piper and I have been friends since we were little, and our moms are best buds with a great love for learning and a huge sense of adventure! They each passed that passion for adventure down to Pavi and me, and we love to travel and tour with our families. Piper and I are old enough now to venture out on our own, and what better way to start than by searching the past and learning about the early humans that existed on this magnificent planet so many thousands of years ago!

First, we'll travel back to 10,000 BCE and learn about early humans with the hunters and gatherers. Next, we'll see how societies grew from small villages to towns. Lastly we will learn how larger cities formed from agriculture and technology!

We study the Mesopotamian region, the birthplace of civilization, highlighting the Sumerian and Babylonian cultures. After that, we're off to the West and the great civilization of Egypt that thrived for thousands of years. Next, we sail the Mediterranean and learn about impactful societies such as the Minoans, the Mycenaeans, and the Phoenicians and their many contributions. Finally, we wrap up with the Greeks and the Romans and how they influenced much of the world as we know it today.

Join us as we embark on a wonderful and exciting adventure back in time and trace our human history by walking in the footsteps of our ancestors. But, Piper, wait! We can't actually travel back in time. Well, that's true, Pavi, but luckily our dads are archaeologists and fantastic storytellers, so we can step into the lives and times of the ancients! So welcome aboard. We're so excited to share this journey with you! Cool, Piper, yes! I can't wait to start. So come on, everyone, let's go explore!

Introduction

WHAT WE'LL COVER

- History vs Archaeology
- Puzzle Pieces in History
- What You Will Learn
- Why You Should Care About History

YOUR ACTION ITEMS

1. Read the Introduction and take notes in your Journal. You can also use the internet, library books, and videos to assist in your research.
2. Review the Terms & Concepts and the Historical and Mythical Figures & Places below.
3. Complete the activities in this chapter.
4. Take the quiz at the end of the chapter of what you learned.
5. Supplemental resources and website links are provided in the Parent-Teacher Guide for additional reading and learning.

STUDENT AIDS

Terms & Concepts

- Artifacts
- Oral traditions
- Civilizations
- Culture

Historical and Mythical Figures & Places

- Herodotus

Chronology of Key Historical Events

10,000 BCE - 476 CE	Time period we're covering in this book.
3500-3000 BCE	Mesopotamia cultures thriving.
484-425/413 BCE	The life and times of Herodotus.
178 BCE	Greek astronomer Eratosthenes accurately calculates the circumference of the Earth.

How Do We Know About History?

Who are some famous archaeologists? Do some online research and list five prominent archaeologists below and what they specifically studied:

1.

2.

3.

4.

5.

The Father of History

The first historian we know of was Herodotus, who often is called the "Father of History." He began writing and preserving events such as wars and battles and people of different cultures by traveling all over Europe, Asia Minor, and Northern Africa to observe and record. Find a picture of Herodotus and either draw and color his image or trace his image and color.

Oral Traditions

Do you and your family have oral traditions? If you do not have any, make one up! Before Herodotus and other historians began recording and writing down these people, places, events, and things, storytelling and oral traditions passed on from one generation to the next were how our ancestors shared their history and the past. Talk to your parent(s) or guardian(s) and have them tell you an oral tradition. Then write a few sentences below to describe the oral practices passed down in your family.

Crossword Puzzle

As we've discussed, history is a puzzle with missing pieces. Sometimes a lot of the puzzle pieces are missing when documents and artifacts are found, so they are not always complete. We must figure them out even when they are incomplete, such as identifying certain artifacts or translating languages. Sometimes when new puzzle pieces are discovered later on, we have to see where they fit in and how they contribute to the whole picture or story.

Complete the crossword puzzle on the next page. Suppose you've never done a crossword puzzle before. In that case, a crossword is a word puzzle usually constructed in a square or rectangular grid with clues that increase our vocabulary and sharpen our brains. The goal is to fill in the white squares with words by solving the clues provided. Two lists of numbered clues accompany the grid, one for the horizontal words that go "across" and one for the vertical words that go "down." The numbers correspond to spaces on the grid where the terms are placed, and the words in the grid cross each other, and that's how we get the name crosswords. You only need a little lateral thinking, quiet time without distractions, and your pen. Have fun and see how you do!

ACROSS

6 an object that is made by a person, especially something of historical or cultural interest

7 a curved piece of glass or plastic that makes things look larger, smaller, or clearer when you look through it

8 the system of communication in speech and writing that is used by people of a particular country or area

10 a state of human society that is very developed and organized

11 history passed down by word of mouth or example from one generation to another (two words)

12 the activity of telling or writing stories

DOWN

1 it means the date is an approximation

2 a particular attitude toward something

3 an official paper, book, or electronic file that gives information about something

4 the study of the past

5 a male sovereign or monarch

6 a guess or estimate

9 a person who excavates sites and examines artifacts

Storytelling

Our picture of history is always, in some way or another, incomplete. It is always one person's story and not everyone's story. If your job was to write the future history of today, whose stories would you tell? It's tempting to say, "Everyone's!" But is that possible? Would it be more important to focus on politics or wars? Religion or education? What about climate change or social media? There is no correct answer here. The choice is yours! Write a short story about your most recent family outing or vacation.

What events did you choose to include? What circumstances did you leave out? Would you be tempted to exaggerate how brave you were in a situation? Or did you leave out any boring parts? How might someone's perception of your outing change based on how you wrote it? How much of the puzzle will you give, and through what lens?

Grammar & Stories

Choose 25 words for the following parts of speech below.

Five Nouns:

Five Compound Words:

Five Adjectives:

Five Verbs:

Five Proper Nouns:

Write a story, play, song, or poem using the words from your list. Read, recite, or sing your masterpiece to your family or friends.

Word Scramble

Unscramble the words below (hint: the terms are in the reading book and glossary)

1 RHIAAGLTCOEOS ____________________

2 ACTIRAFT ____________________

3 EIHGMASGL ____________________

4 ULSMCUOB ____________________

5 VETEPRCPIES ____________________

6 OLZIIIANCTVI ____________________

7 NENCIAT ____________________

8 HYRITSO ____________________

9 LARNCEDA ____________________

10 EMENITIL ____________________

11 OCBUOITNNITR ____________________

12 UEPZZL ____________________

13 YTSRO ____________________

14 PEEOLP ____________________

15 MOOTARSENR ____________________

16 OYGOEHNCTL ____________________

17 DYSTU ____________________

18 NOERMTVGNE ____________________

19 USLPECUTR ____________________

20 LGAEGUNA ____________________

Name Your Price

You are a historian who sells puzzles of historical artifacts. Each puzzle has 350 puzzle pieces. Each puzzle piece costs $0.03 to make, plus $1.00 for the puzzle box. Labor to package the puzzle costs $7 per person per hour. Each worker can put together four puzzles per hour. You can sell the puzzles for 45% more than it costs to make them. See the Parent -Teacher Guide for instructions on breaking down a word problem into easy steps.

Q1. What is your cost to make each puzzle? Calculate on the line below, and then write the answer on line A2 below.

(Materials and labor x number of puzzle pieces) + cost of box + (cost per person per hour ÷ number of puzzles put together per hour).

Hint: Remember, Multiply and Divide BEFORE you Add!

Q2. What is the price you will charge for each puzzle? Calculate on the line below, and then write the answer on line A1 below.

Cost of the puzzle x 1.45

Hint: for this problem, round down. Example. 3.223 = 3.22

Q3. How much money will you will make on each puzzle? Calculate on the line below, and then write the answer on line A3 below.

Price - Cost

A1. Price charged for one puzzle __________

A2. - Cost to make one puzzle __________

A3. = money you make from one puzzle __________

Congratulations! You are a successful puzzle maker.

Artifacts

Do an internet search for the word artifacts. Below your search term, change the search results from "All" to "Images." Review the images, sketch your favorite artifacts, or insert pictures of artifacts that the archaeologists have discovered and color them. If you have access to software, create a slide show and narrate and record a tour of the artifacts.

The Ages of History

The Ice Age began 2.4 million years ago and lasted until c. 12,000 BCE. As the glaciers melted, continents formed, and we began to see human life in these prehistoric times.

The Ice Age is where human development emerges, but there is overlap that can be confusing. For our purposes, Archaeologists break down our early human history into three ages:

1. The Stone Age
2. The Bronze Age
3. The Iron Age

From there, historians and archeologists divide the Stone Age into three periods:

1. Paleolithic Era
2. Mesolithic Era
3. Neolithic Era

Around 12,000 BCE, when the last Ice Age ended, humans entered the Middle Stone Age or Mesolithic era. The development of agriculture is considered the dividing line between the Mesolithic and the Neolithic periods. The Stone Age ended when someone learned that you could melt metal and fashion it into tools and weapons, ushering in the Bronze Age in or around 3,000 BCE.

Research one of the ages or eras listed above and write about what you learned. What were your favorite tools? How could you use them today?

What's Different?

Find the 7 differences in the pictures below, then add your own artistic touches to the illustrations and color.

Introduction Quiz

Fill in the Blank

1. A person who studies history is called a ______________________________ .
2. ______________________________ are people who excavate sites to study artifacts.
3. ______________________________ is also known as the "Father of History."
4. The Epic of Gilgamesh was considered the ______________ piece of written literature.
5. History always has all of the pieces of the 'puzzle,' true or false? ______________
6. ______________ are verbally passed down through generations.

7. Circle the correct answer. The Queen of Egypt, Cleopatra, was:

An Egyptian   A Greek   A Roman

8. What are we going to learn about in this book?

____

____

____

____

____

9. Why should we care about History?

____

____

____

____

____

Chapter 1 - Becoming Civilized

WHAT WE'LL COVER

- Civilizations formed from nomadic hunter- gatherer societies
- Elements that all civilizations have in common
- How civilizations grew and thrived
- The causes why civilizations fall

YOUR ACTION ITEMS

1. Read Chapter 1, Becoming Civilized, and take notes in your Journal. You can also use the internet, library books, and videos to assist in your research.
2. Review the Terms & Concepts and the Historical and Mythical Figures & Places below. Also, review the Area Map and Chronology of Key Historical Events for better understanding.
3. Complete the activities in this chapter.
4. Take the quiz at the end of the chapter of what you learned.
5. Supplemental resources and website links are provided in the Parent-Teacher Guide for additional reading and learning.

STUDENT AIDS

Terms & Concepts

- Agriculture
- Code of Hammurabi
- Ice Age
- Nomads
- Propaganda
- Reeds
- Shaduf
- Embalming
- Hunter-Gatherers
- Stereotypes
- Threshing
- Winnowing

Historical and Mythical Figures & Places

- Catal Huyuk
- Gordon Childe
- The Seven Wonders
- Jericho
- King Hammurabi
- Philo
- Sargon the Great

Area Map

Chronology of Key Historical Events

2,600,000 BCE	Earliest stone tools found.
12,000 BCE	Ice Age ended, and Middle Stone Age or Mesolithic era begins.
10,000-9000 BCE	New Stone Age and Neolithic period starts and the development of agriculture begins in the Middle East.
8000-7000 BCE	The city of Jericho is established.
6700-5600 BCE	The dawn of civilizations born and Neolithic settlement Catal Huyuk in modern-day Türkiye (Turkey) formed.
4000 BCE	Farming begins in Northern Europe.
3000 BCE	Stone Age ends and the Bronze Age begins with metal fashioned into tools and weapons.
2300 BCE	Emperor Sargon the Great rules in Mesopotamia.
1771 BCE	King Hammurabi of Babylon organizes laws for every possible crime or dispute.
353/352 BCE	King Mausolus of Caria dies and mausoleum tombs born.
280 BCE	The Lighthouse at Alexandria erected.
225 BCE	Philo writes travel guide book called On the Seven Wonders.

Our Stone Age Ancestors

Humans inhabited the earth long before advanced civilizations progressed. Evidence suggests that human use of fire goes as far back as 1.8 million years ago, and over 400,000 years ago, early humans used fire in hearths. Fire provided protection from animals, warmth, and the ability to cook food. So let's get cooking! Find the ingredients, cook an "authentic" recipe, and note how it came out.

List the ingredients available to early humans:

Then search for or create a recipe using some of these ingredients.

How did it turn out? Did it taste good or not so great? Bad? Was it easy to cook or hard? Did you have difficulty finding some ingredients? Did you substitute or change the recipe in any way?

Prehistoric Cave

Hunter-gatherers were nomadic and lived in small groups. Using natural resources such as caves and cliffs to provide shelter, hunter-gatherers began making huts and tents using bones and wood for support. Make a model of a prehistoric cave. Consider how the inside should look. What would be around the cave? What does the land look like outside of the cave? Is a body of water nearby, such as a river, lake, or ocean? Collect these materials and prepare your project work surface:

1. Cardboard
2. Colored Paper
3. Clay and/or mud
4. Dirt and/or sand
5. Grass, leaves, and/or twigs
6. Rocks or pebbles
7. Paint or brush
8. Water
9. Cotton balls
10. Figurines
11. Craft paints
12. Colored pencils
13. Markers
14. Glue or adhesive
15. Scissors

The instructions for this activity are in the Parent-Teacher Guide. Take a picture of the final product and paste it below.

Hunter-Gatherer Societies

Hunter-gatherers made tools out of stone, bone, antlers, ivory, sticks, and other items in their environment. Some oldest tools include sharpened stones and bones used to puncture, chop, cut, and scrape. Draw a picture of the tools used by hunter-gatherers.

How would you use these tools today?

The Ages of History

The food eaten by hunter-gatherers varied depending on where they lived. Their diet included meat from animals and fish and food plants, including vegetables from the roots, leaves, and stems, along with fruit, seeds, and nuts. Using the internet or field guides, research local native plants, fungi, and animals that are edible. Then, get outside, look in your yard or neighborhood park, and list the foods you would find if you were a hunter-gatherer.

1. ______
2. ______
3. ______
4. ______
5. ______
6. ______
7. ______
8. ______
9. ______
10. ______
11. ______
12. ______
13. ______
14. ______
15. ______
16. ______
17. ______
18. ______
19. ______
20. ______

Word Search

Circle the words from the list below. The words may be placed horizontally (forward or backward), vertically (up or down), or diagonally.

```
R O B A L F O N O I S I V I D J H T D D Y
K I C R A F T S M A N Z Y D B A Y T J J C
T N B O J J L J Y L T D T R M K X R Q L L
P F B V L M Y W M M G Y L M Z X A O A X G
L R G N R I T Y J D R Z U Q Q R H S Q N M
T A E R G E H T N O G R A S C C S N K J G
E S S B B J Q P T Z A P Y H I Z M J D X P
X T W T W P J P R B J X I R I B G R A B T
P R M C N D R L I R P T E N J N Y D B V P
L U A O Z E D O Y N E J N R I V M K Y D R
O C R N N G M M P C G O X M D I Q H W G J
R T T Q P O B U T A V B L V N M C P V N L
A U I U E K T U N A G A R I Q R B G Z L M
T R S E T D R H T O B A S T A Y Z R L P N
I E A S K E A I E M M T N R Y R Q M G Y R
O Y N T N M O R E I R D E D Y W V Q B W Z
N B S S L N V D T A S I L X A Y P R N Q B
G R X M P Q J Q T D H T B N W L G X N Y N
L X V D V N T I N P N M I X B L T Q Y L J
Z L N X B W O P J B G J T C T M K J G Z R
V G T N J N M N J L R X L Y V Q X T L L L
```

ADMINISTRATION	CLASS	DIVISION OF LABOR	HAMMURABI
INNOVATION	MONUMENTS	SARGON THE GREAT	ARCHITECTURE
CONQUESTS	EMBALMING	HIERARCHY	JERICHO
PHILO	TRADE	ARTISANS	CRAFTSMAN
EXPLORATION	INFRASTRUCTURE	MONOTHEISTIC	PROPAGANDA

Wonder While You Wander

In 225 BCE, a man named Philo wrote a book called On the Seven Wonders. Review the reading book or do some online research and write down below these seven wonders of the world on Philo's list.

1. ______
2. ______
3. ______
4. ______
5. ______
6. ______
7. ______

Which is your favorite Wonder and why?

Complete the Sentence

1. A ________________________ structure or hierarchy is one of the trademarks of civilization.
2. Hammurabi provided a well-managed ____________________ and generous infrastructure.
3. A butcher, a baker, and a candlestick maker represent a ________________________ .
4. The ____ stated laws for crimes and disputes.
5. Without ____ , civilization will not progress.
6. Ancient Civilizations built __________________________________ to appease their gods.
7. ____ was a Mesopotamian ruler.
8. The ____ built strong homes for the people.
9. The Seven Wonders of the World included masterpieces of ________________________ .
10. Romans emperors loved to brag about their war ____________________________ .
11. ________________________ is a step in the mummification process and is still used today.
12. More complex civilizations have a ______________ with the most powerful people on top.
13. The city of ____________________________ takes the prize for the oldest city wall.
14. A man named ____________________________ wrote a book called On the Seven Wonders.
15. Ancient cities ______________ their surplus food/supplies for items they do not produce.
16. An __________________________ was hired to make a hand-crafted tool for the farmer.
17. Further __________________________________ underground may reveal more artifacts.
18. Roads are a lasting example of ancient ____________________________________ .
19. Some cultures are ______________________________________ and worship only one god.
20. Romans used art as ______________________________ to promote their point of view.

administration	conquests	hierarchy	monuments
architecture	craftsman	infrastructure	Philo
artisan	division of labor	innovation	propaganda
class	embalming	Jerico	Sargon the Great
Code of Hammurabi	exploration	monotheistic	trade

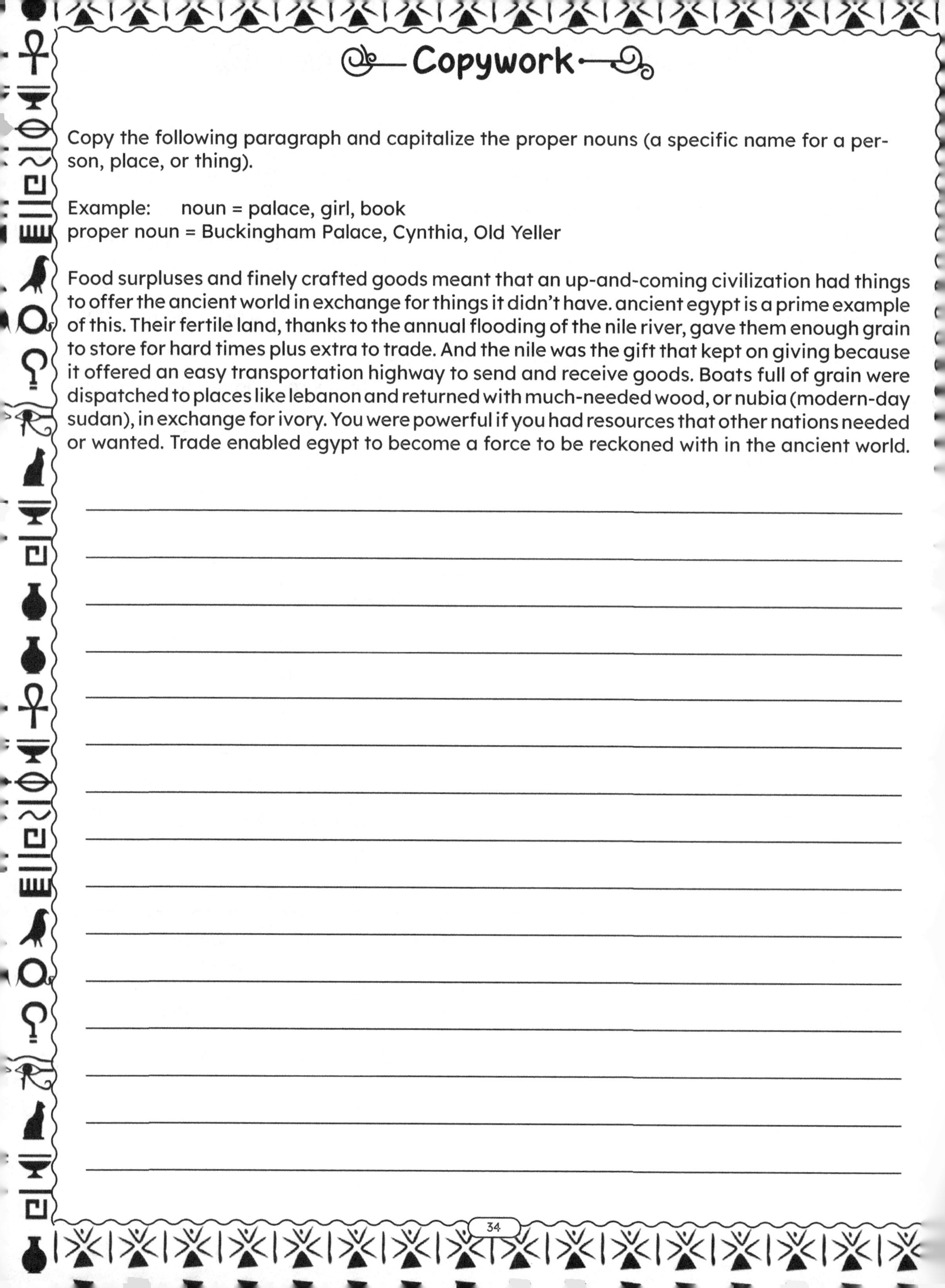

Copywork

Copy the following paragraph and capitalize the proper nouns (a specific name for a person, place, or thing).

Example: noun = palace, girl, book
proper noun = Buckingham Palace, Cynthia, Old Yeller

Food surpluses and finely crafted goods meant that an up-and-coming civilization had things to offer the ancient world in exchange for things it didn't have. ancient egypt is a prime example of this. Their fertile land, thanks to the annual flooding of the nile river, gave them enough grain to store for hard times plus extra to trade. And the nile was the gift that kept on giving because it offered an easy transportation highway to send and receive goods. Boats full of grain were dispatched to places like lebanon and returned with much-needed wood, or nubia (modern-day sudan), in exchange for ivory. You were powerful if you had resources that other nations needed or wanted. Trade enabled egypt to become a force to be reckoned with in the ancient world.

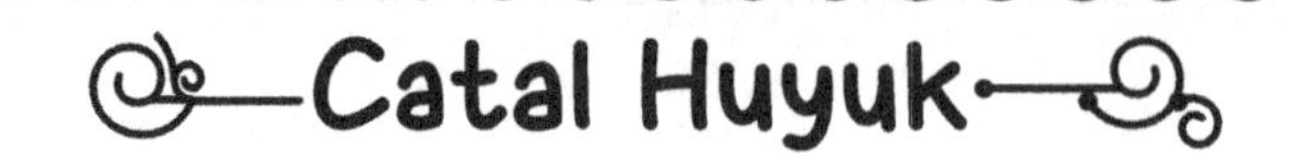

Catal Huyuk

One of our best examples of a Neolithic settlement is Catal Huyuk in modern-day Turkey, which dates back to between 6,700 and 5,600 BCE at the dawn of civilization. Research and create a diorama inside a village home showcasing how the Catal Huyuk people lived. Include how they cooked, ate, worked, and played. You can also have where they prayed and buried their family members. A diorama is a three-dimensional tool used to enhance your learning experience. A diorama appeals to the senses and tells a story. It's a good idea to plan when creating the story, but there are no limits to your creativity! Collect these materials and prepare your project work surface:

1. Base: shoebox, tissue box, or similar box
2. Paint
3. Crayons, colored pencils, or markers
4. Construction paper
5. Blocks: plastic foam, cardboard, Legos, etc.
6. Figurines: Legos, dolls, miniatures, paper figures, etc.
7. String (if needed)
8. Glue stick, Elmer's glue, or adhesive
9. Tape
10. Filler material: cotton balls, batting, paper, etc.
11. Scissors
12. The Ancient Civilizations reading book (optional)
13. A computer for research
14. Printer (not necessary)

The instructions for this activity are in the Parent-Teacher Guide. Take a picture of the final product and paste it below.

Tinker Tools

You live in the Mesolithic period, and you make and sell stone farming tools. Business is really growing since the ice has melted. Each tool costs $4.75 in materials. It takes two hours to make one tool, and you work eight hours each day. Show your work on each line below. See the Parent -Teacher Guide for instructions on breaking down a word problem into easy steps.

Q1. How many tools can you make in one eight-hour day?

___

hours per day ÷ # hours per tool = # tools a day

Q2. Your customer just ordered 80 tools. Using your answer to Q1, how many eight-hour days will it take you to complete this project?

___

tools ordered ÷ # tools a day = number of days to complete this project

Q3. Your tools have become even more popular, so you hire five helpers. Each helper can make one tool every 4 hours. How many tools can all of your helpers make in each eight-hour day?

___

(# hours per day ÷ # hours per tool = # tools a day per helper) x number of helpers = number of tools made by all of your helpers.

Hint: Remember to calculate within the parentheses first.

Q4. Using your answers above, how many tools in total can be made in each eight-hour day by you and all of your helpers?

___

tools you make + # tools your helpers make = total tools per day

The Seven Wonders of the World

We've learned about Philo's Seven Wonders of the Ancient World. Now, it's time to build them, or, at least, our best blocky version of them! Let's build this in Minecraft. Follow the Minecraft project instructions in the Parent-Teacher Guide.

Draw and color a picture of each Wonder below.

Chapter 1 Quiz

What are the three causes of civilization collapse? Give specific examples you read about.

1. ______________________________

   a. ______________________________

   b. ______________________________

   c. ______________________________

   d. ______________________________

2. ______________________________

   a. ______________________________

   b. ______________________________

   c. ______________________________

   d. ______________________________

3. ______________________________

   a. ______________________________

   b. ______________________________

   c. ______________________________

   d. ______________________________

Chapter 2 - The Sumerians

WHAT WE'LL COVER

- The Mesopotamian region
- The rise of civilization and the impact of agriculture
- How Sumerian societies were organized
- Sumerian writing and religion
- Sumerian decline and collapse

YOUR ACTION ITEMS

1. Read Chapter 2, The Sumerians, and take notes in your Journal. You can also use the internet, library books, and videos to assist in your research.
2. Review the Terms & Concepts and the Historical and Mythical Figures & Places below. Also, review the Area Map and Chronology of Key Historical Events for better understanding.
3. Complete the activities in this chapter.
4. Take the quiz at the end of the chapter of what you learned.
5. Supplemental resources and website links are provided in the Parent-Teacher Guide for additional reading and learning.

STUDENT AIDS

Terms & Concepts

- The Cradle of Civilization
- Cuneiform
- Scribe
- Lugal
- Shrines
- Ziggurat
- Tell or tel
- Temple cities
- Aristocrats
- The Eridu Genesis
- The Sumerian King List
- Dynasty
- Mythology
- Cylinder seal
- Sargon Legend
- Deification

Historical and Mythical Figures & Places

- Mesopotamia
- The Mediterranean Sea
- The Persian Gulf
- The Tigris
- King Utu-Hegal
- King Alulim
- King Lugalzagesi
- Gilgamesh

- The Euphrates
- The Fertile Crescent
- The Elamites
- Etana
- Queen Kubaba
- Tell al-`Ubaid

Area Map

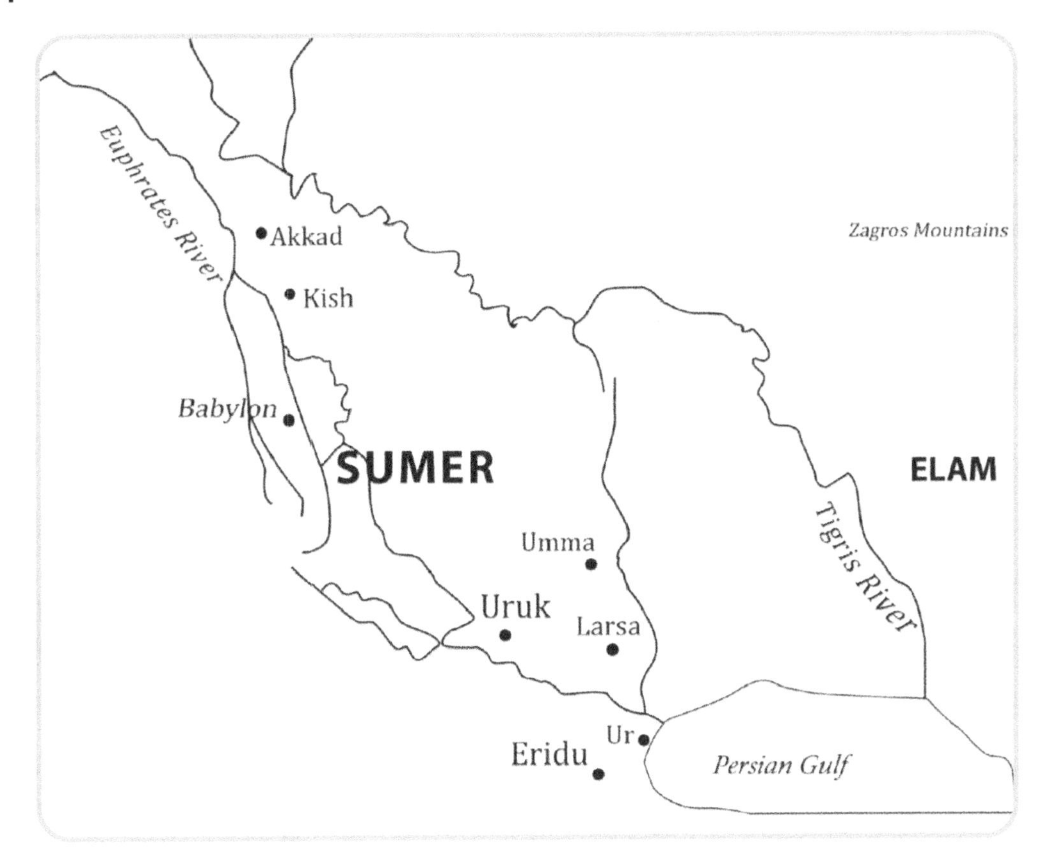

Chronology of Key Historical Events

5,000 BCE	Mesopotamia civilizations on the rise.
5000-4100 BCE	The Ubaid Period.
4100-2900 BCE	The Uruk Period - the cities of Uruk, Eridu, Kish, and Ur thrive.
3600 BCE	The Lugal replaces King as a permanent head-of-state position.
3500-3300 BCE	Writing evolved by the Sumerians.
2900-2334 BCE	The Early Dynastic Period forms in Sumer and Akkad.

2900 BCE	The Great Flood in Sumer.
2700 BCE	The Epic of Gilgamesh written.
2500 BCE	Kubaba, Queen of Kish, in power.
2334-2218 BCE	The Akkadian Period.
2218-2047 BCE	The Gutian period emerges and invades and overthrows the Akkadian empire.
2100 BCE	The Sumerian King List is written.
2047-1750	The Ur III Period.
1400 BCE	The Sumerians develop a hymn written in cuneiform.

Mesopotamian Rulers

Queen Kubaba was the only female to be recorded in the King's List. Read the article by ThoughtCo., "Kubaba, A Queen Among Kings," or find a book at the library and then write a report about Queen Kubaba below.

You will find the link to the article in the Parent-Teacher Guide.

Let's Bake! Cuneiform Writing

Historians call the Sumerian form of writing cuneiform, which means "wedge-shaped." By about 3100 BCE, Sumerians learned that a symbol could stand for a sound rather than just an object. This marked the beginning of a true alphabet. The Sumerians developed words from a combination of phonetic sounds and could spell any word and convey complex emotions or abstract thoughts, not just tangible things. At this point, the number of symbols they used dropped from about 1,000 characters for things to only 600 symbols for sounds.

Take the space below and draw some of your picture writings to communicate in Sumerian society. We provide a link in the Parent-Teacher guide from the J. Paul Getty Museum. Watch the video on how to make cuneiform cookies. Or you can follow your own recipe. Then get to baking!

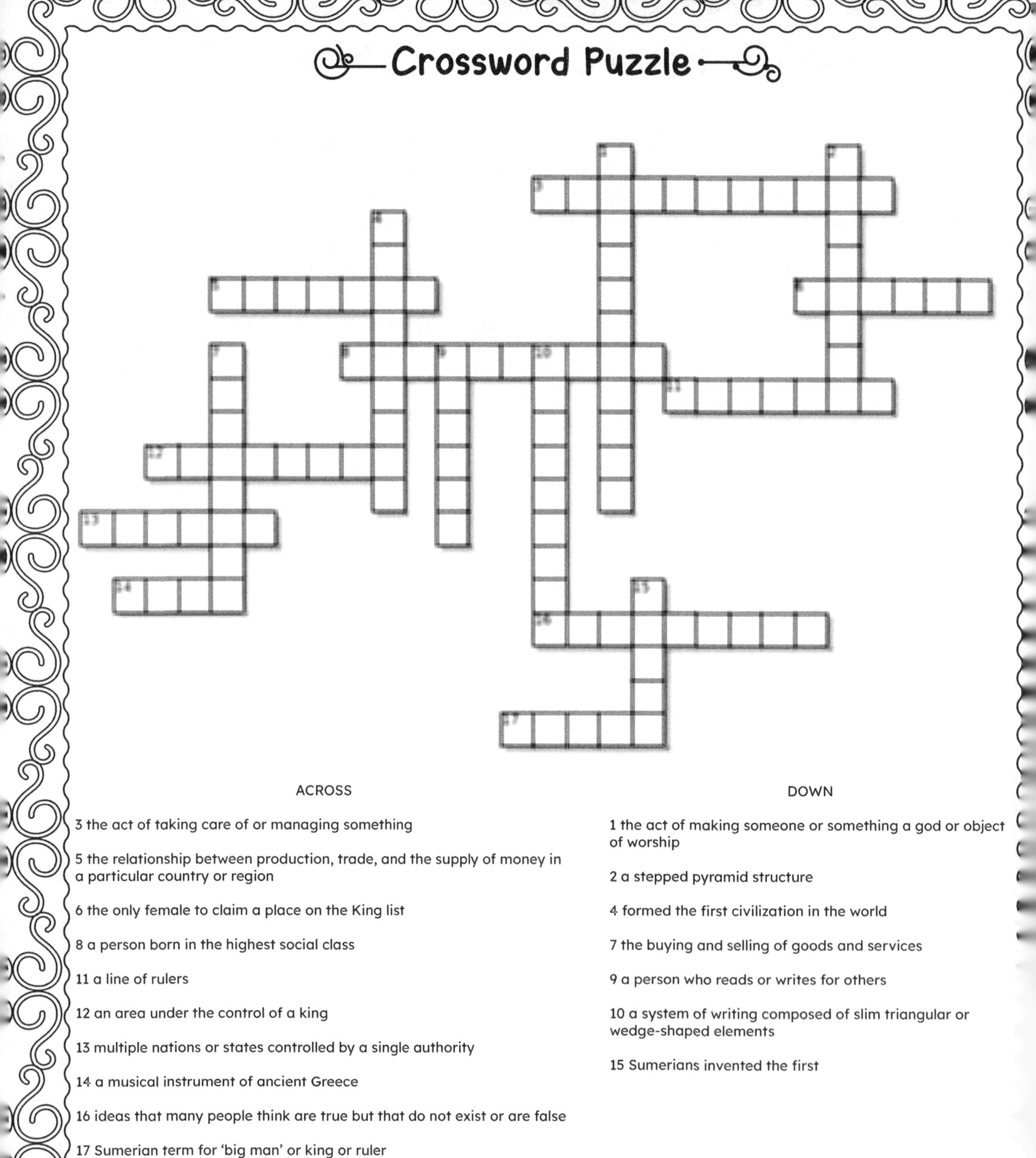

ACROSS

3 the act of taking care of or managing something

5 the relationship between production, trade, and the supply of money in a particular country or region

6 the only female to claim a place on the King list

8 a person born in the highest social class

11 a line of rulers

12 an area under the control of a king

13 multiple nations or states controlled by a single authority

14 a musical instrument of ancient Greece

16 ideas that many people think are true but that do not exist or are false

17 Sumerian term for 'big man' or king or ruler

DOWN

1 the act of making someone or something a god or object of worship

2 a stepped pyramid structure

4 formed the first civilization in the world

7 the buying and selling of goods and services

9 a person who reads or writes for others

10 a system of writing composed of slim triangular or wedge-shaped elements

15 Sumerians invented the first

Identification Card

In ancient Mesopotamia, your cylinder seal was your identification card. You would use it as a signature on official documents. Seals were cylinder-shaped and usually carved out of stone. Everyone had one, from kings to slaves, and every person's seal was different. Your seal was carved with your unique combination of animals, gods, geometric figures, or writing. If your seal was very nice, it would be cut backward as a mirror image. This way, the designs would appear correct when you rolled your seal across wet clay. They were pretty small—three to four inches tall at the most. Draw below your cylinder seal to identify yourself. What does it look like? What will you include on your card? Don't forget to decorate it!

The Great Flood

Write a story below about you and what your personal experiences during the Great Flood would be if you were living in ancient Sumerian times. What happened to you? How did you survive? Who and what did you take with you?

Mesopotamian Home Life

Early Sumerian houses were originally constructed from reeds in the marshes, bundled together. And then eventually, they were made from mud and bricks mixed with straw, which were baked, or sundried. Average families had single-story homes, but wealthy families might have had larger homes with their bedrooms on a second story. The courtyard was the center of family life. Sumerians believed that rooms that opened into each other were bad luck, but rooms that opened to the outdoors were good luck. So a house had several rooms that opened into a central courtyard, letting light in since windows were rare. A household—consisting of your parents, siblings, and maybe other close family members or slaves—would work, play, and eat there. In a Sumerian home, there would have been a bathroom with a drain to let waste water run out, a kitchen with a fireplace or oven and cooking utensils, a shrine where the family would worship, bedrooms, and a reception room where visitors would be entertained and sleep. A ladder would usually lead to the roof, where a family might sleep when the weather was hot.

Research images of a Sumerian home. Then draw a slide show of your Sumerian home, including some of the abovementioned features.

Inventions and Achievements

Archaeologists have confirmed that ziggurats were some of the world's first observatories. The first early astronomers mapped the constellations, could tell the difference between planets and stars, and realized that the Earth moved around the Sun.

List the planets in order from closest to furthest from the Sun.

____

____

____

____

____

____

Draw the solar system or make a model of the solar system. There are so many options for this project that you can make it as creatively simple or as detailed and complex as you'd like! Links to helpful sites and the instructions for this activity are in the Parent-Teacher Guide.

What's Different?

Find the 11 differences in the pictures below, then add your own artistic touches to the illustrations and color.

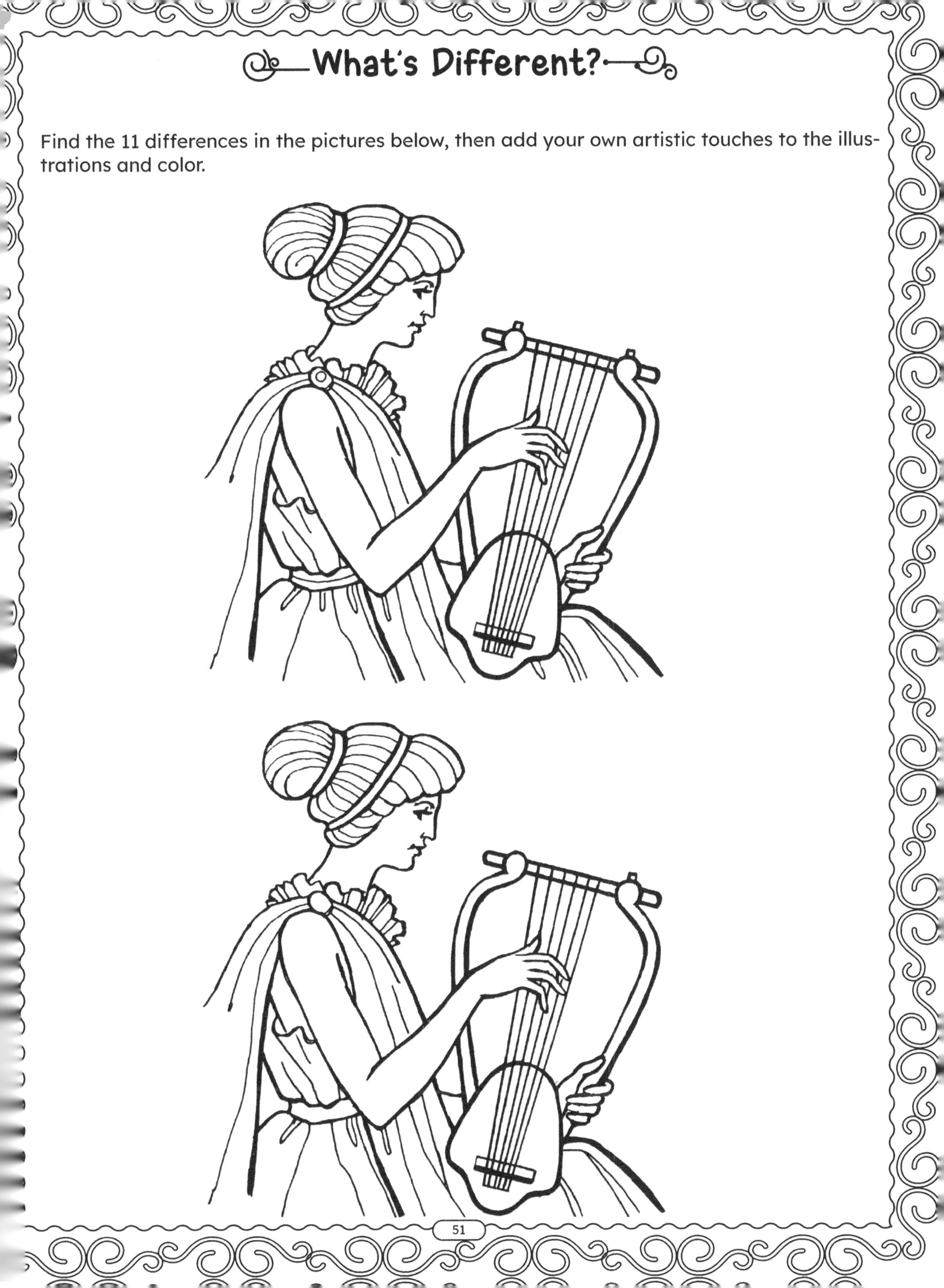

Grammar & Stories

Choose 25 words for the following parts of speech below.

Five Nouns:

Five Compound Words:

Five Adjectives:

Five Verbs:

Five Proper Nouns:

Write a story, play, song, or poem using the words from your list. Your theme is the Sumerian Renaissance. Read, recite, or sing your masterpiece to your family or friends.

Building Big Ships

You are a Sumerian business owner. Your company builds ships to sell to your customers. Since the great flood, business has been booming. The price you charge for each ship is 15,000 gold coins. The cost to build each ship is 30% of your price. You would like to know how much money you have made for January, February, and March. See the Parent -Teacher Guide for instructions on breaking down a word problem into easy steps.

Q1. If you make and sell 20 ships in January, 30 ships in February and 40 ships in March, what are your total sales for January to March combined? Calculate on the line below then write the answer on line A1 in the table.

___

(# January + # February + # March = total ships) x price per ship = total sales.

Hint: calculate inside the parenthesis first.

Q2. Using the information above, what is your cost to build all of the ships from January to March? Calculate on the line below then write the answer on line A2 in the table.

___

Total sales x .30 = cost to build all of the ships

Q3. When you deduct the cost of the ships from your total sales, that is the money you have left to pay for your business expenses like advertising and insurance. What is the money you have left to pay your business expenses? Calculate on the line below then write the answer on line A3 in the table.

___

Total sales - total cost to build ships = money left to pay expenses

Q4. Your business expenses totaled 84,000 in January, 126,000 in February, and 168,000 in March. Calculate your business expenses for January - March and then write the answer on line A4 in the table.

___

Expenses January + Expenses February + Expenses March = total expenses

Q5. After you pay your business expenses, what is left is your money before tax. Calculate on the line below then write the answer on line A5 in the table.

___

Money left to pay expenses - total expenses = money before tax

Q6. Now that you know how much money your company made, Shulgi of Ur needs his tax money so he can maintain the city. Your tax rate is 40% of your money before tax. How much tax will you pay? Calculate on the line below then write the answer on lines A6 and A7 in the table.

___

Money before tax x .40 = tax you will pay

Q7. The money left after you pay your taxes is the money you get to keep. What is the money you get to keep? Calculate on the line below then write the answer on line A8 in the table.

___

Money left before taxes - tax = the money you get to keep

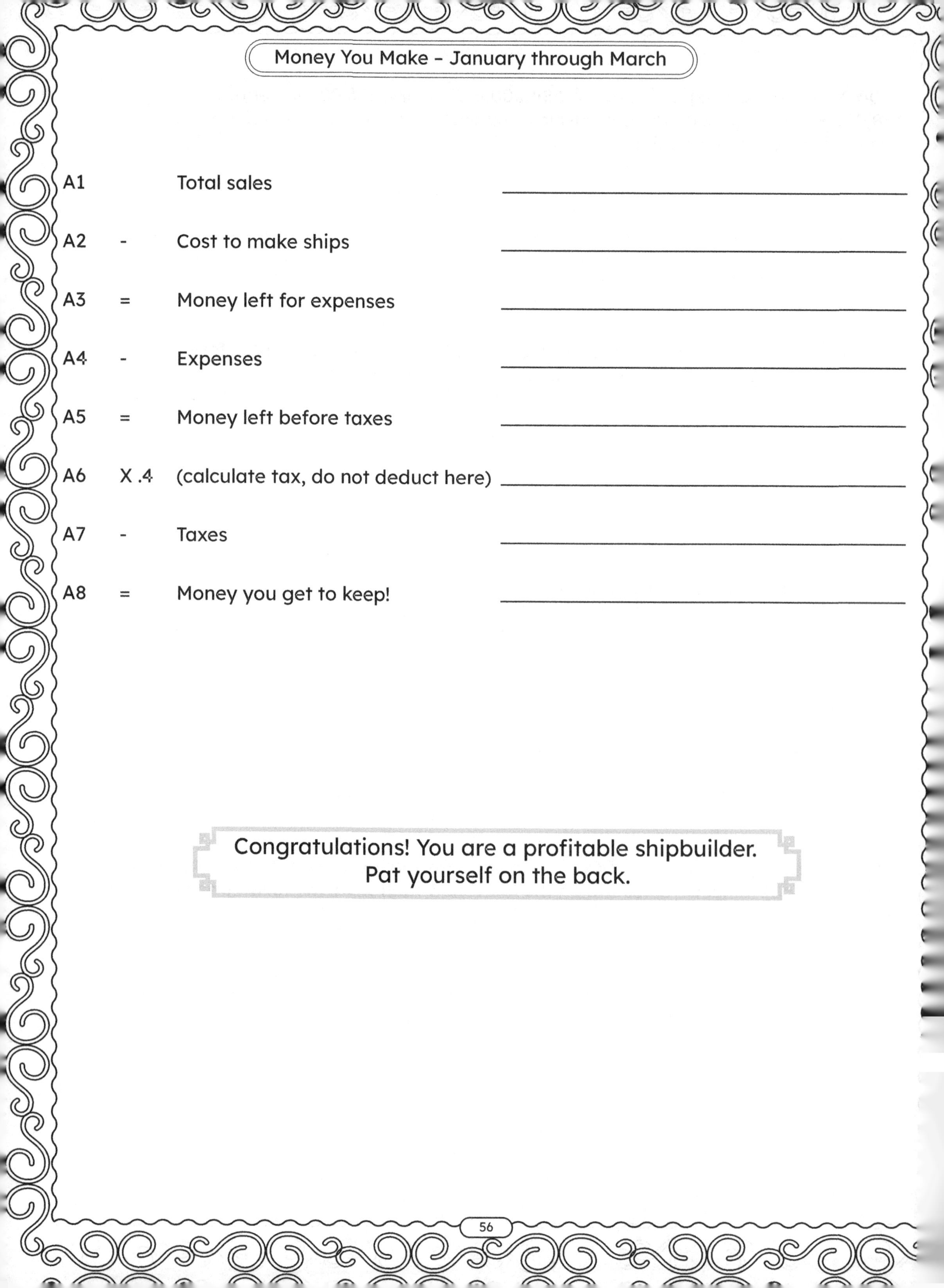

Money You Make – January through March

A1		Total sales	______
A2	-	Cost to make ships	______
A3	=	Money left for expenses	______
A4	-	Expenses	______
A5	=	Money left before taxes	______
A6	X .4	(calculate tax, do not deduct here)	______
A7	-	Taxes	______
A8	=	Money you get to keep!	______

Congratulations! You are a profitable shipbuilder.
Pat yourself on the back.

Scrapbook

Create a scrapbook, vision board, poster board, or online board like Pinterest to showcase your favorite topics that resonated with you in this chapter. Create your board with online images, or if you're creating a physical board, use images from magazines, words or phrases, or pictures you draw and color and display them on your board. Then at the end of this workbook, combine them into a single board and save your collection.

Chapter 2 Quiz

1. What modern-day countries in the Middle East and Southwestern Asia make up the Mesopotamia region?

2. What forms the Fertile Crescent in Mesopotamia?

3. What is Mesopotamia also called, and why is it called that?

4. Where did the Sumerians live in Mesopotamia?

5. How did the Sumerians come to exist?

6. What made the Sumerians unique?

7. What contributions did the Sumerians leave for future generations?

8. What happened to the Sumerians in the end?

Chapter 3 - The Babylonians

WHAT WE'LL COVER

- Babylonia location in Mesopotamia
- How the Babylonian civilization was formed
- Babylonian culture, learning, and advancements
- King Hammurabi and his code of laws
- King Nebuchadnezzar II and The Golden Age
- Babylonian fall and collapse

YOUR ACTION ITEMS

1. Read Chapter 3, The Babylonians, and take notes in your Journal. You can also use the internet, library books, and videos to assist in your research.
2. Review the Terms & Concepts and the Historical and Mythical Figures & Places below. Also, review the Area Map and Chronology of Key Historical Events for better understanding.
3. Complete the activities in this chapter.
4. Take the quiz at the end of the chapter of what you learned.
5. Supplemental resources and website links are provided in the Parent-Teacher Guide for additional reading and learning.

STUDENT AIDS

Terms & Concepts

- Akitu Festival
- Amytis
- Babel
- The Battle of Opis
- Bureaucracy
- Cosmopolitan
- Delegate
- Etemenanki
- Etiology
- Iconized
- Kha b'Nissan
- Legal Code
- Monolith
- Nisannu

Historical and Mythical Figures & Places

- Alexander the Great
- King Ashurbanipal
- The Hammurabi Code
- Cyrus the Great
- The Hittites
- The Ishtar Gate
- The Kassites

- The Elamites
- King Esarhaddon
- King Hammurabi
- King Nebuchadnezzar
- King Sennacherib
- King Sumuabum

Area Map

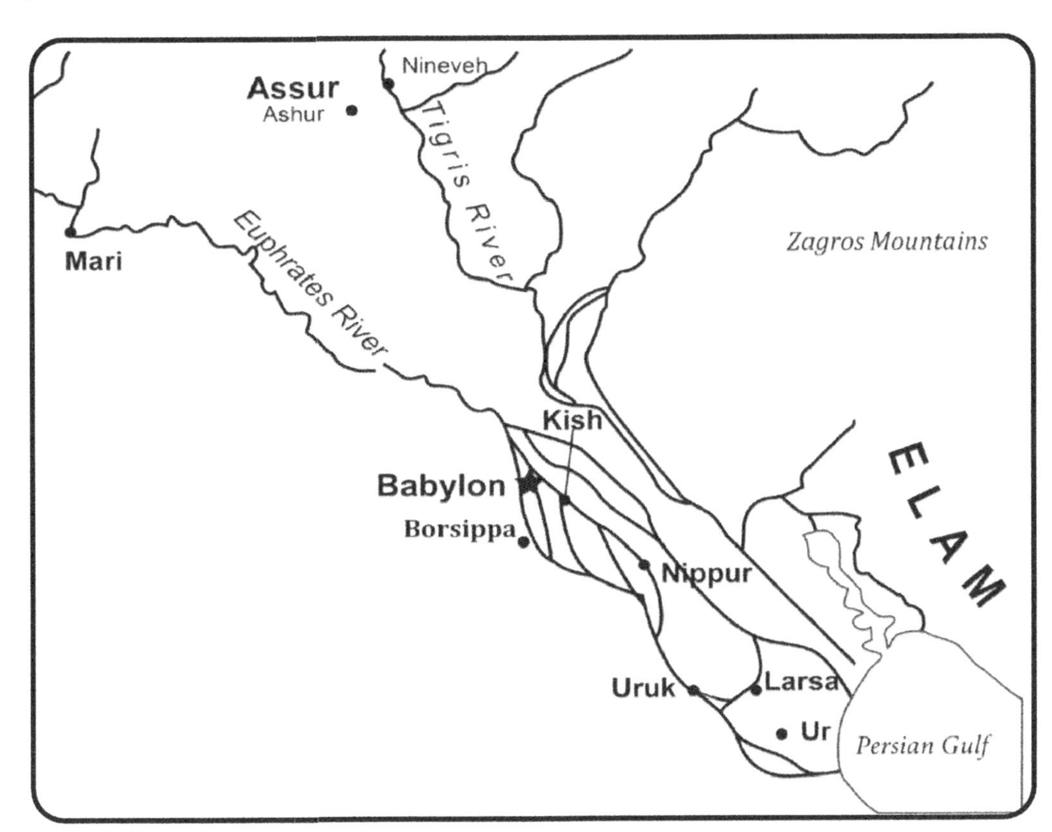

Chronology of Key Historical Events

2300 BCE	The city of Babylon forms.
1894 BCE	Babylon becomes the capital of a small kingdom in southern Mesopotamia ruled by the Amorite king, Sumuabum.
1810 BCE	King Hammurabi is born.
1792 BCE	The Empire of Babylonia emerges with Hammurabi taking the throne.
1775 BCE	Hammurabi controls all of Mesopotamia.
1771 BCE	King Hammurabi writes The Hammurabi code of 282 laws.

1765 BCE	The Elamites conspire to start a war between Babylon and a neighboring kingdom, Larsa.
1761 BCE	Hammurabi conquers Elam, Larsa, and Mari.
1750 BCE	The Babylonian empire begins to unravel.
1595 BCE	The Hittites sack the city of Babylon.
1225 BCE	The Kassites, led by King Tukulti-Ninurta, take Babylon from the Hittites and temporarily rename the city Karanduniash.
705 BCE	Sennacherib comes to the Assyrian throne.
681 BCE	Sennacherib's son, Esarhaddon, takes the Assyrian throne and rebuilds and restores Babylon.
668 BCE	Esarhaddon's son, Ashurbanipal, comes to the Assyrian throne as one of the last of the great Assyrian kings and constructs a great library.
627 BCE	Ashurbanipal dies and the Assyrian Empire falls apart.
626 BCE	King Nabopolassar takes over Babylon.
605-604BCE	Nebuchadnezzar II, comes to power in Babylonia, expands the empire and makes Babylon the greatest city in the world.
539 BCE	Babylonia falls to the Persian king Cyrus the Great during the Battle of Opis, liberating the exiled Jews.
331 BCE	Alexander the Great conquers Babylon.
323 BCE	Alexander the Great dies in Babylon.

Babylonian Hanging Gardens

The Babylon Gardens are one of the seven wonders of the ancient world, but unfortunately, we don't have any examples since they no longer exist. Legend has it that King Nebuchadnezzar built the gardens as a gift for his foreign wife, Amytis, who, in the flat arid landscape of Mesopotamia, missed her lush mountain home. Although this is a romantic story, there are some suspiciously missing pieces.

Create a hanging garden using the materials below. Take a picture of your completed garden and paste it below. Gather the following materials and prepare your project workspace:

1. A floral foam block
2. Cream or tan craft paint
3. Play sand
4. Tools: wooden skewer, spoon, wooden craft sticks, etc.
5. Small silk flowers and greenery and actual flower cuttings and greenery
6. Tacky craft glue
7. Knife, utility knife
8. Cutting board
9. Paintbrush
10. Paper plates for paints and sand

The instructions for this activity are in the Parent-Teacher Guide. Draw a picture of your creation or paste a picture of it below.

The Tower of Babel and Language

Both Hebrew and Christian texts tell the story of the Tower of Babel. To prevent the people from building a tower to heaven, God confused their language so the people could not understand each other. This story is an example of an etiology, a narrative designed to explain the source or cause of something - like different nations speaking diverse languages.

English is part of the Indo-European language family in the West Germanic group. German and Dutch are part of the same group. A link for Google Translate is in the Parent-Teacher Guide. Use the provided link, or your favorite translator, then translate each noun into German and then into Dutch.

	English	German	Dutch
1	House		
2	Automobile		
3	Song		
4	Animal		
5	List		
6	Book		
7	Desk		
8	Clock		
9	Water		
10	Ocean		

How are the words the same? How are they different?

If you had to learn German or Dutch, which would you choose and why?

The Ishtar Gate

The Ishtar Gate was an amazing structural piece of architecture built by the Babylonians by the order of King Nebuchadnezzar II around 575 BCE. The eighth gate led to the inner city of Babylon and was walled on either side. You can watch two videos to learn more about the Ishtar Gate and the Processional Way on exhibit at the Pergamon Museum in Berlin, Germany. Links for the videos are in the Parent-Teacher Guide. Or find a library book about the Ishtar Gate and read about this fascinating piece of architecture.

Then get creative by doing one of the following:

1. Sketch your version of a particular artifact or feature.
2. Create a slideshow below of the artifacts or features you see in the videos or your book.
3. Narrate and record a guided tour of the famous Ishtar Gate.

Authentic Babylonian Foods

Babylonian Master Chefs wrote their recipes in cuneiform on clay tablets, and four of them still exist today and are on exhibit at Yale University. We've provided a video link in the Parent-Teacher Guide of the Yale team cooking three recipes (as best they could interpret them). You won't want to miss it!

Then choose your favorite lamb or vegetable stew and make it for your family. A link to the Yale version of the lamb stew recipe can be found in the Parent-Teacher Guide if you want to try it.

Did you follow the Yale recipe? If so, did you make any substitutions? If you chose another recipe, how was it different? How did your recipe turn out? Would you make it again?

Akitu Festival

You live in ancient Babylon and today is a super exciting day because you and your family are attending the Akitu Festival. Do some research on the Akitu Festival, a helpful link is provided in the Parent-Teacher Guide. Write a story about your experiences. What did you see? What events took place? What did you eat?

The Code of Hammurabi

King Hammurabi had a very forward-thinking solution for administering justice. In 1771 BCE, he organized laws for every possible crime or dispute along with their punishments called the Code of Hammurabi. Today we have what are called penal codes, broken down into categories of criminal law (committing a crime) and civil law (rights of individuals).

Do some research and find the penal code (criminal code) for your country. Hint: a search for "(name your country) statutes," and you should find the website for your country's laws.

1. What is your country's definition of theft?

____

2. What is the title and chapter for theft?

____

3. What is your country's definition of trespass?

____

4. What is the title and chapter for trespass?

____

5. Did you find your country's list of penal codes easy to navigate (find what you are looking for)?

____

6. What are the names of your country's top leaders? (i.e. President/Vice President; Prime Minister/Deputy Prime Minister)

____

Word Search

Circle the words from the list below. The words may be placed horizontally (forward or backward), vertically (up or down), or diagonally.

```
B E T A G R A T H S I M K M V V T
U K C Y N N D E Z I N O C I X A M
R U D O N O E H T N A P Y S E Y N
E D D P S D X R Y E Q D I R B K N
A R D T L M E D H G M P G G G N Y
U A L T M L O I L V O E U R W G T
C M V E I Q T P M F H L N T T T B
R Y T E G T Y N O T E A O A I K Z
A M F M I A O E R L S S H I N K L
C S W T N L L E D S I T A I T K A
Y Z E Q Y T D C Y E I T S G Y E I
M S R B T N R R O L L A A B I R G
X M A A A N I V O D N E X N P L R
Z B B X K A Y N T N E L G Y L M A
T Y E R N Z O X U B N B R A T W N
R L Z S X M Z Y T J Y Y K M T J L
A N W W R Q R Y J Y R K B Y B E R
```

BABYLON
MARDUK
MONOLITH
ETEMENANKI
BATTLE OF OPIS

ETIOLOGY
ICONIZED
BUREAUCRACY
ISHTAR GATE
HITTITES

RELIEFS
LEGAL CODE
ALEXANDER THE GREAT
AKITU
ASSYRIANS

PANTHEON
COSMOPOLITAN
ESAGILA
DELEGATE
NISANNU

Word Match

Review the terms and definitions below and match the number on the left to the definition on the right.

1 Babylon	________________	the proper name for the ziggurat
2 Etiology	________________	took Babylon during the Battle of Opis
3 Relief	________________	a narrative designed to explain the source or cause of something
4 Pantheon	________________	to give part of your work, power or authority to somebody in a lower position than you
5 Marduk	________________	the ensemble of a culture's religious figures
6 Icon	________________	a form of sculpture where the design is raised from a usually flat background
7 Legal code	________________	containing people of different types or from different countries, and influenced by their culture
8 Cosmopolitan	________________	Marduk's annual festival to ring in the new year
9 Monolith	________________	sacked Babylon in 1595 BCE
10 Bureaucracy	________________	a glazing technique
11 Cyrus the Great	________________	a government or organization's system of rules and ways of doing things
12 Esagila	________________	March or April in Babylon
13 Etemenanki	________________	the temple where Marduk's statue stood
14 Akitu	________________	means Gate of God or Gate of the gods
15 Delegate	________________	poem tells how Marduk defeated chaos to bring the earth into existence and order
16 Hittites	________________	Hammurabi destroyed this city-state
17 Mari	________________	a collection of rules that include punishments for non-compliance
18 Nisannu	________________	a person or thing that is revered or idolized
19 Enuma Elish	________________	the chief god of the Babylonians
20 Faience	________________	an obelisk, column, large statue, etc., formed of a single block of stone

Copywork

Read and copy the following paragraph. Circle the pronouns (words that replicate nouns).

Example: Jack and Jill really like coloring books, so **they** color **it** every day.

At one point, there were three layers of walls surrounding the city. Since Babylon straddled the Euphrates, the river would have passed directly under the walls and out the other side. Many visitors to Babylon, including our friend Herodotus, wrote about these walls, and each one measured them very differently. We don't know exactly how tall or wide they were or how many miles they ran around the city. However, we do know that they had an impact on just about everyone who saw them. One account says the walls were 22 feet thick with a 10-foot wide passage between each layer. Another description puts them at more like 33 feet wide and 66 feet tall, with towers at different points even taller. Herodotus goes even further, saying they were 80 feet thick and 320 feet high. Good ol' Herodotus. Just enough facts to make you think it may be true and just enough hyperbole to make you wonder if it's not. His account is thought to be an exaggeration. Still, many agree that you could drive a chariot with four horses along the top and even turn around!

Babel Budget

(This is a multi-page problem) You run a Babylonian household. Your job is to manage the money that comes in and out of the home by following your budget. A budget is a document you create to manage your money by listing how much you earn and how you will spend your earnings. You understand the importance of savings and investment, so you allocate your earnings with 50% going to necessary expenses (things you need), 30% to extra expenses (things you like), and 20% to investments and savings for your future. As a builder, you bring home 15,000 gold coins for designing great walls and Ishtar gates.

These are the cash transactions that occur each month. Calculate and place the correct amounts in the budget worksheet.

Total Cash In 15,000

Necessary expenses (50% of total cash in):

a. Calculate necessary expenses and enter on line 1

____

Total cash in x .50 = necessary expenses

Mortgage: 30% of necessary expenses (given) = 2,250.00

b. Calculate food & household expenses (= mortgage) and enter on line 2

____

Mortgage = food and household expenses

c. Calculate clothes & personal care (1/2 of mortgage) and enter on line 3

____

Mortgage ÷ 2 = clothes & personal care

d. Calculate insurance (8% of necessary expenses) and enter on line 4

____

Necessary expenses x .08 = insurance

e. Calculate transportation (=clothes & personal care) and enter on line 5

Transportation = clothes and personal care

f. Calculate education (25% of insurance) and enter on line 6

Insurance x .25 = education

Extra Expenses (30% of total cash in)

g. Calculate extra expenses (30% of total cash in) and enter on line 7

Total cash in x .30 = extra expenses

h. Calculate restaurants & entertainment (50% of extra expenses) and enter on line 8

Extra expenses x .50 = restaurants & entertainment

i. Calculate Vacations (1/4 extra expenses) and enter on line 9

Extra expenses ÷ 4 = vacations

j. Calculate gifts and donations (25% of extra expenses) and enter on line 10

Extra expenses x .25 = gifts

Investments & Savings (20% of total cash in)

k. Calculate investments & savings (20% of total cash in) and enter on line 11

____

Total cash in x .20 = investments & savings

l. Calculate investments (50% investments & savings) and enter on lines 12

____

Investments & savings x .50 = investments

m. Calculate savings (1/2 investments and savings) and enter on lines 13

____

Investments & savings ÷ 2 = savings

Total Cash Out

n. Calculate total cash out (sum of all expenses) and enter on line 14

____

Necessary expenses + extra expenses + investments and savings = total cash out

(Hint: total cash in is the same number as total cash out. If it is not, recheck your work)

Congratulations! You are a responsible money manager.

Time to Relax & Color

Scrapbook

Create a scrapbook, vision board, poster board, or online board like Pinterest to showcase your favorite topics that resonated with you in this chapter. Create your board with online images, or if you're creating a physical board, use images from magazines, words or phrases, or pictures you draw and color and display them on your board. Then at the end of this workbook, combine them into a single board and save your collection.

Chapter 3 Quiz

1. How did the Babylonians come to exist?

2. What made the Babylonians unique?

3. What type of building projects were they known for?

Chapter 4 - Egyptian Civilizations

WHAT WE'LL COVER

- Egypt's location in Africa and the importance of the Nile River
- The Egyptian religion, the worship of gods, and the afterlife
- The Great Pyramid at Giza and the Lighthouse at Alexandria
- Egyptian hieroglyphic writing

YOUR ACTION ITEMS

1. Read Chapter 4, Egyptian Civilizations, and take notes in your Journal. You can also use the internet, library books, and videos to assist in your research.
2. Review the Terms & Concepts and the Historical and Mythical Figures & Places below. Also, review the Area Map and Chronology of Key Historical Events for better understanding.
3. Complete the activities in this chapter.
4. Take the quiz at the end of the chapter of what you learned.
5. Supplemental resources and website links are provided in the Parent-Teacher Guide for additional reading and learning.

STUDENT AIDS

Terms & Concepts

- The Book of the Dead
- Capstone
- Coffin Texts
- The Crook
- Faience
- Frontalism
- The Flail
- Hieratic Writing
- Hieroglyphics
- Canopic Jars
- Ideograms
- Pyramid Texts
- Sarcophagus
- Scales of Justice
- Shabti Dolls
- Vizier

Historical and Mythical Figures & Places

- King Akhenaten
- Amun or Amun-Ra
- Bastet
- Field of Reeds
- The Hall of Truth
- Ra
- Set
- Sneferu

Area Map

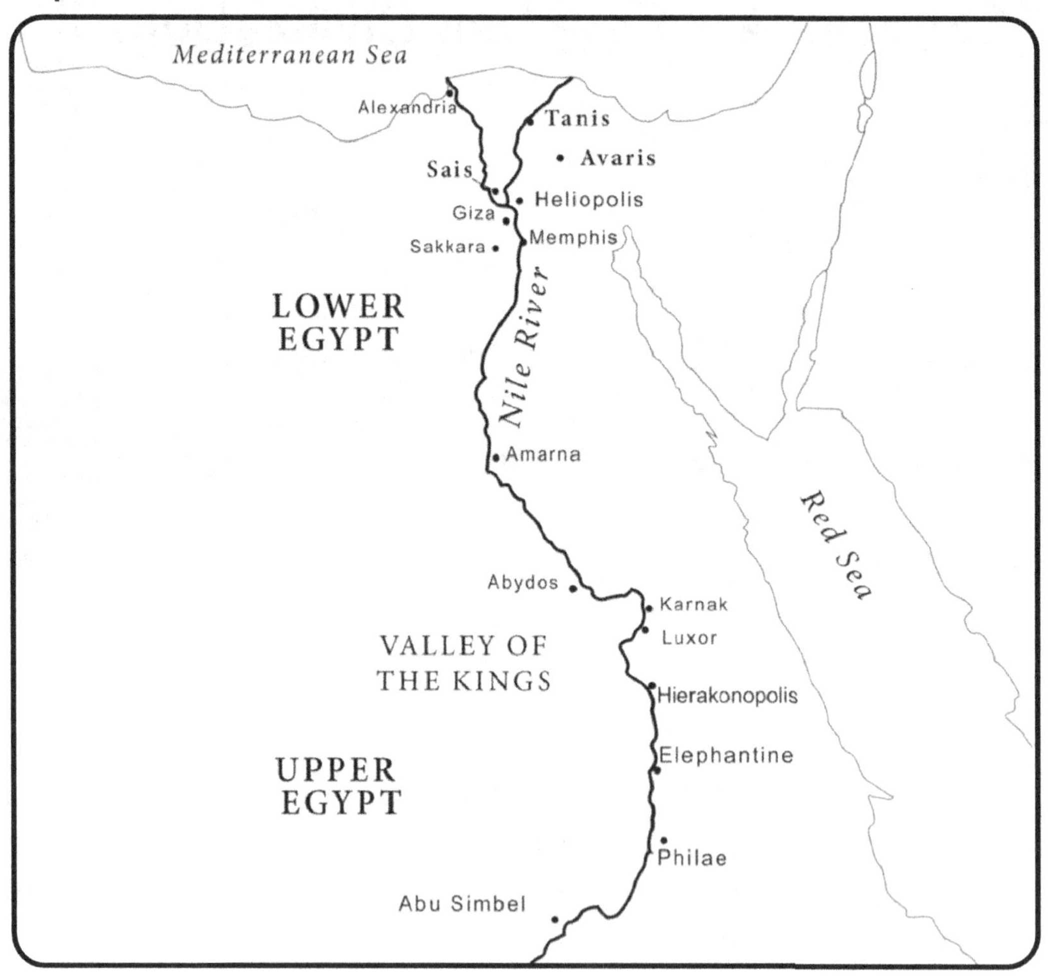

Chronology of Key Historical Events

5600 BCE	Egyptian civilization begins.
3100 BCE	Hieroglyphics developed.
2400-2300 BCE	Pyramid Texts written on the walls of Egyptian royal tombs.
2134-2040 BCE	Coffin Texts start to be engraved onto the coffins.
1550-1070 BCE	The Book of the Dead developed in tombs.
900 BCE	Pharaoh becomes a common term name for the Egyptian king.
331 BCE	Alexander the Great founds the city of Alexandria.
642 CE	Arabs take over the city of Alexandria.
640 CE	Egypt is captured by the Arabs and converted to the religion of Islam, ending their long run as one of the great ancient civiliza-tions.

Triangles

Pyramids are common around the world. They have a low center of gravity, and they are very sturdy structures. They frequently appear in nature, like trees and mountains, and humans still use triangle shapes in buildings to this day.

Below are different types of triangles.

Equilateral triangle
has three equal sides

Isosceles triangle
has two equal sides

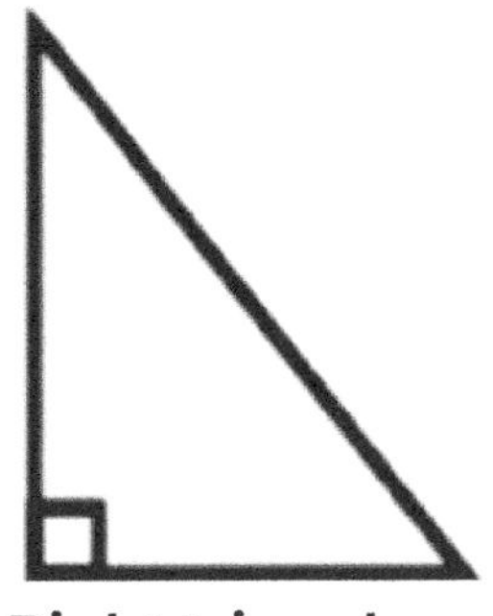

Right triangle
has one angle = 90°

Acute triangle
has three angles < 90°

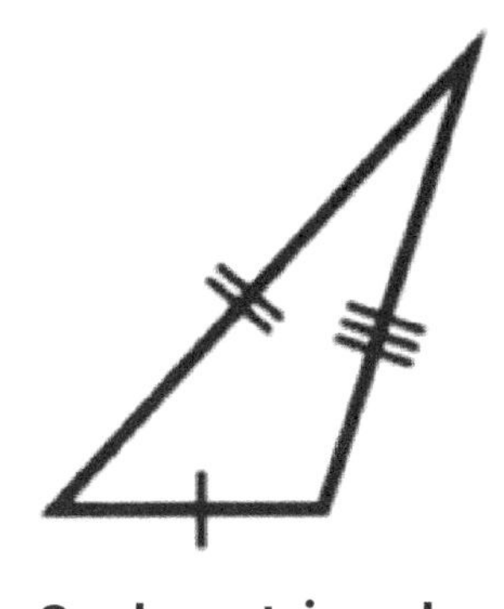

Scalene triangle
has no equal sides

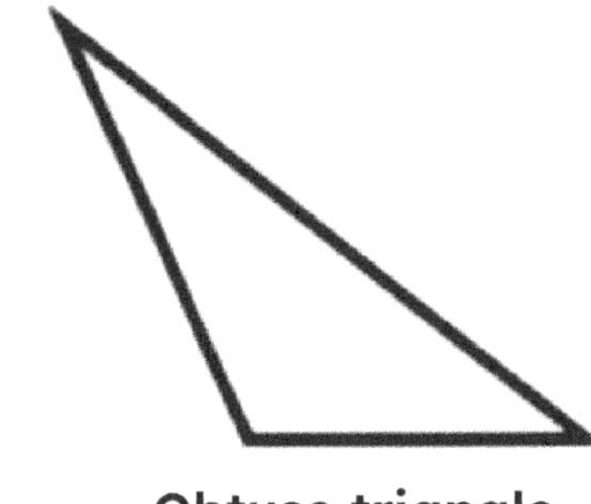

Obtuse triangle
has one right angle > 90°

Go on a field trip downtown or a nature walk. If you do not live by a city, town, or park, walk through your neighborhood, your home. Do you see any triangles?

Take pictures of all structures where you can identify triangles and create a scrapbook, vision board, poster board, or online board like Pinterest to showcase them. Were there any triangles you did not see? Why do you think you could not find them?

A Pyramid Tomb Floor Plan

We all know that the Egyptians built magnificent pyramids for the Pharaohs and their gods, surrounded by all the luxuries of life that they could enjoy in the afterlife. When King Tut's tomb was discovered and opened in 1922, the archaeologists found beds, clothing, jewelry, food, boats, statutes, chests, and even a throne. All of these items were housed in different chambers and rooms, including the burial chamber, treasure room, antechamber, annex, and passageways.

Using the space below, draw a pyramid floor plan. Include the rooms and items stored in these rooms and what hieroglyphics will appear on the pyramid walls.

What's Different?

Find the 5 differences in the pictures below, then add your own artistic touches to the illustrations and color.

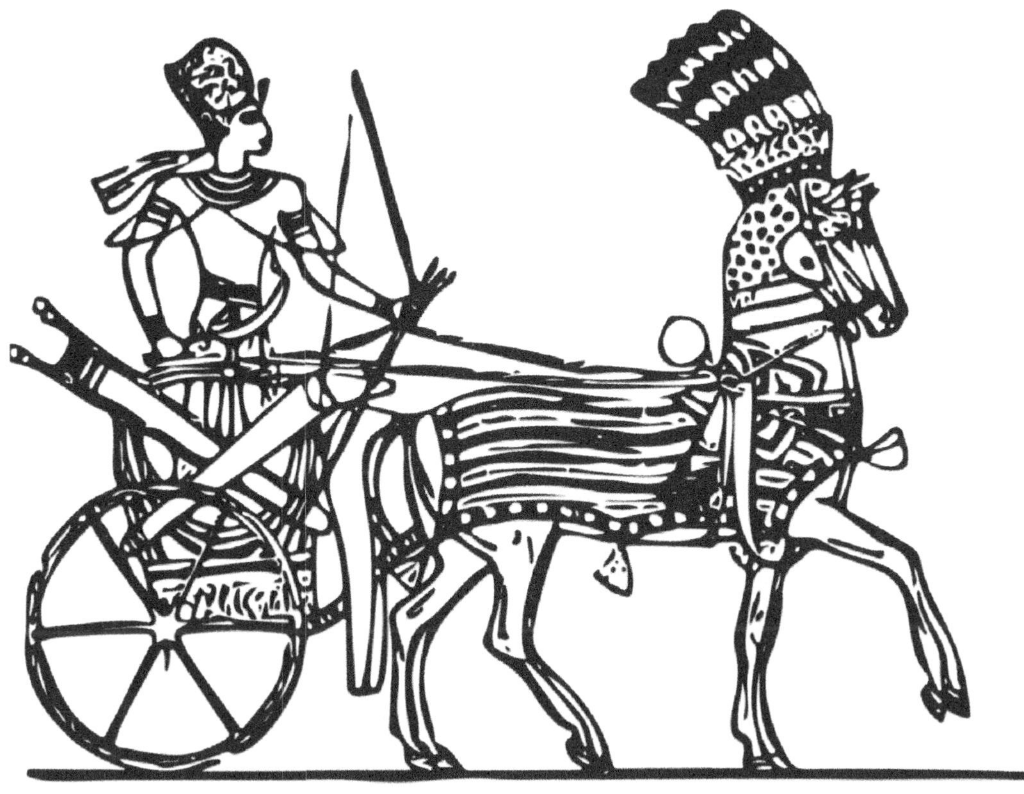

Video of Egypt for Kids

Watch a video or find a library book to learn more about ancient Egypt. We've provided some helpful links in the Parent-Teacher Guide.

Then get creative by doing one of the following:

1. Sketch your version of a particular artifact or feature.

2. Create a slideshow below of the artifacts or features you see in the video.

3. Narrate and record a guided tour of one of the famous pyramids.

Making Egyptian Paper

One of the Egyptians' greatest inventions was paper. The Egyptians used the stems of a papyrus plant to create the piece and put multiple sheets together to form scrolls. A papyrus plant can grow up to 13 feet tall and, in addition to paper, was used to make sandals, hats, ropes, floor mats, boats, and baskets.

The inside of the stems of the papyrus plant was called the pith, which was sliced or cut into skinny strips. These strips were laid side by side and overlaid, forming a weave pattern. A cloth was placed over the layers and hit with a mallet to compress the strips. Then the piece was dried, polished with a stone, and sheets put together to form a scroll.

If papyrus isn't available where you live, we can make papyrus from brown paper bags! Collect these materials and prepare your project work surface:

1. 3 brown paper bags (lunch bags)
2. Paper plates or bowls
3. Paper Towels
4. Aluminum Foil
5. Wax Paper
6. Rolling pin
7. Scissors
8. Water
9. Glue Elmer's Glue or Adhesive

The instructions for this activity are in the Parent-Teacher Guide.

Writing Egyptian Hieroglyphics

The Egyptians created the picture writing we know as hieroglyphics. The hieroglyphic writing system was a combination of logograms (images that capture the essence of the word it stands for), and phonograms (a picture that stands for a spoken sound), and ideograms (pictures that stand for an idea or concept).

Use the hieroglyphic alphabet below to write your name, your family's names, and your friends' names on the next page.

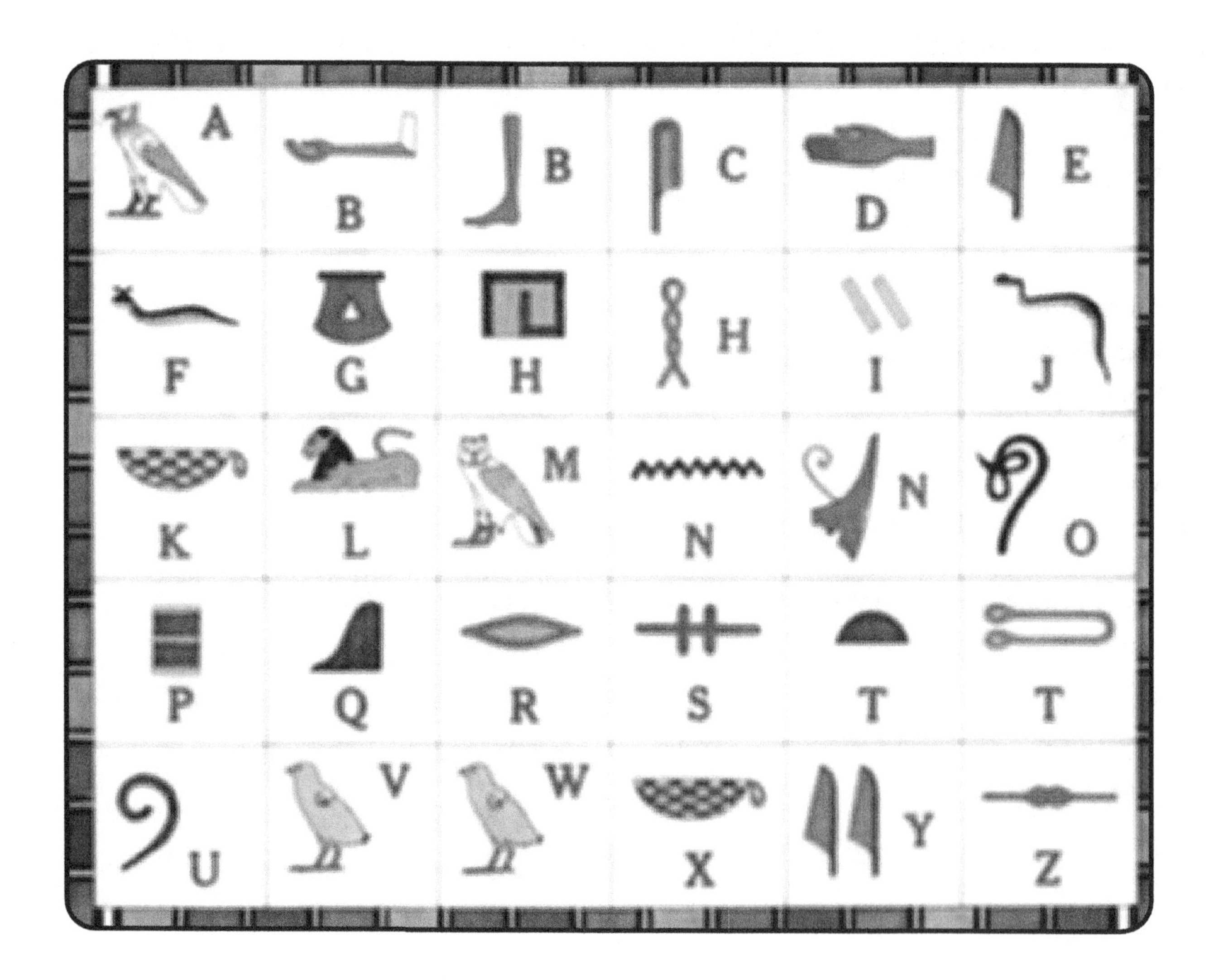

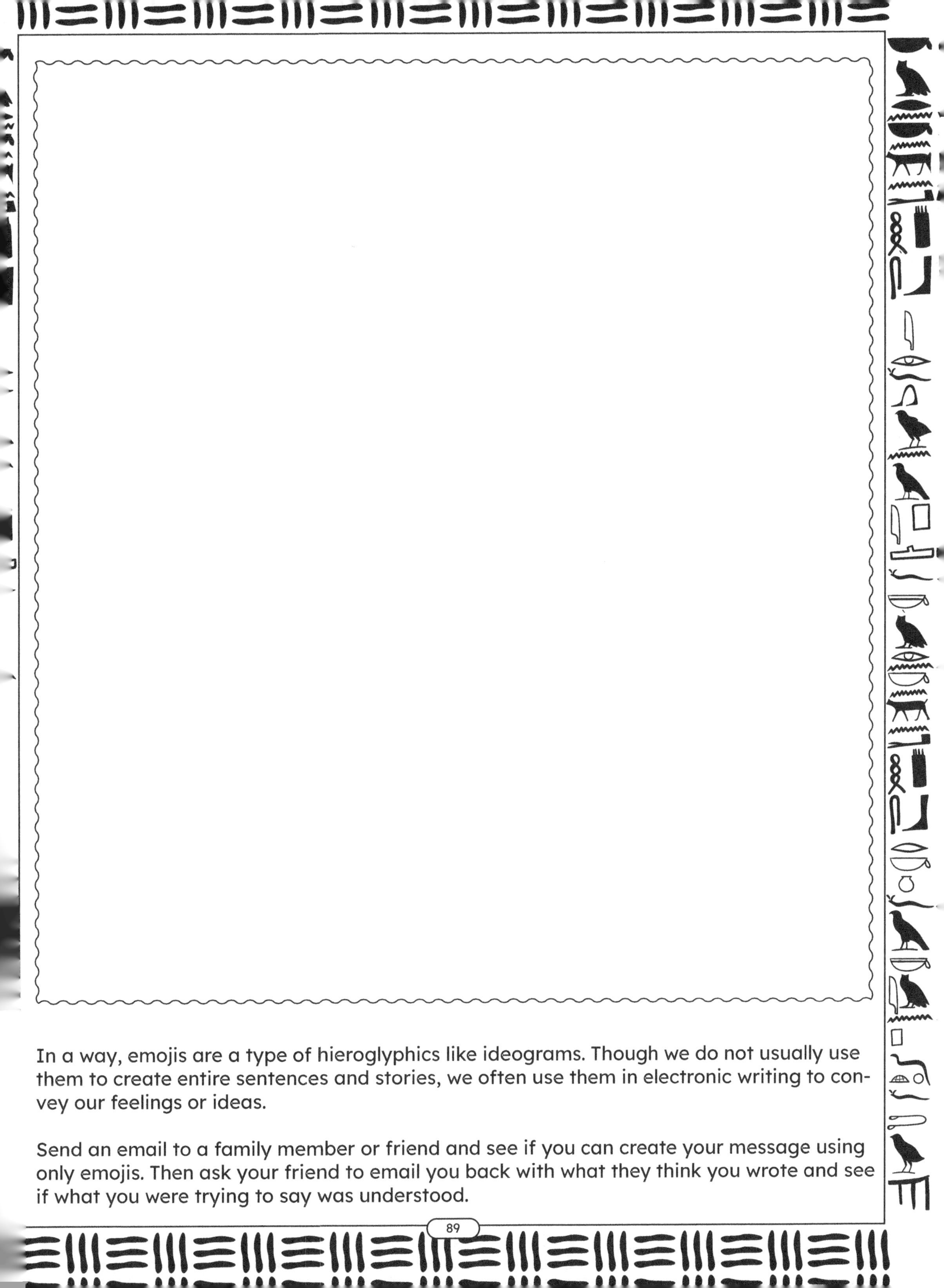

In a way, emojis are a type of hieroglyphics like ideograms. Though we do not usually use them to create entire sentences and stories, we often use them in electronic writing to convey our feelings or ideas.

Send an email to a family member or friend and see if you can create your message using only emojis. Then ask your friend to email you back with what they think you wrote and see if what you were trying to say was understood.

Piles of Pyramids

You are an Egyptian living in the time of the pyramids and own a business. Your company builds pyramids to sell to your customers. The cost to make each stone is 1.50 gold coins in materials and labor. You need to pay each of your workers 5 gold coins per day to build the pyramid. Each pyramid will have 2346 stones and requires a crew of ten workers and 30 working days to complete. You can sell the pyramids for 42% more than it costs to make them. See the Parent-Teacher Guide for instructions on breaking down a word problem into easy steps.

Q1. What is your cost to make each pyramid? Show your work below.

___

(Cost to make each stone x the number of stones) + (the daily price per person X the number of people working each day X the number of days to complete one pyramid) = cost for each pyramid.

(Hint: Remember, multiply BEFORE you add!)

Q2. What is the price you will charge for each pyramid?

___

Total cost X 1.42 = price for each pyramid

Q3. How much money will you make on each pyramid?

___

Price - cost = money you make on each pyramid (also the money you make for one crew)

Q4. If you have five crews of laborers working and you sell all of the pyramids you make, how much money would you make in 30 working days?

___

Money you make for one crew x 5 = total money you would make in 30 days

Q5. How many crews would you need to work for 30 days to make $35,835.66?

___

Total money to make ÷ money made per crew = number of crews needed

Crossword Puzzle

ACROSS

4 a division or contrast between two groups or things that are completely opposite to and different from each other

10 a tall pointed stone column with four sides, put up in memory of a person or an event

12 an early version of paper was made from this plant

13 Egyptian god of the sun and creator of the universe, also known as Ra

16 glazed earthenware or pottery, especially a fine variety with highly colored designs

17 what the Egyptians referred to as one's physical body

18 worshipping many gods and goddesses

20 the longest river in the world

21 a casket often crafted to look like the person inside

DOWN

1 a word commonly used for a king of Egypt, which originally referred to the king's palace or house

2 human-headed canopic jar that holds the liver

3 to preserve a dead body by treating it with special oils and wrapping it in cloth

5 a form of writing using pictures

6 a striped headcloth worn by kings in ancient Egypt

7 the worship of one god

8 you see this artistic technique used in hieroglyphics to represent the best individual part of the body

9 simple tomb for a king made of mud bricks (before pyramids)

11 an Egyptian ring engraved with fourth and fifth names outlined by an oval

14 an Egyptian god depicted as a man with the head of a jackal

15 a small fertile or green area in a desert region, usually having a spring or well

19 a name for a region or province in Egypt

Grammar & Stories

Choose 25 words for the following parts of speech below.

Five Nouns:

Five Compound Words:

Five Adjectives:

Five Verbs:

Five Proper Nouns:

Write a story, play, song, or poem using the words from your list. Your theme is the Egyptian religion. Read, recite, or sing your masterpiece to your family or friends.

Scrapbook

Create a scrapbook, vision board, poster board, or online board like Pinterest to showcase your favorite topics that resonated with you in this chapter. Create your board with online images, or if you're creating a physical board, use images from magazines, words or phrases, or pictures you draw and color and display them on your board. Then at the end of this workbook, combine them into a single board and save your collection.

Chapter 4 Quiz

1. How did the Egyptians come to exist?

2. What made the Egyptians unique?

3. What contributions did the Egyptians leave for future civilizations?

Chapter 5 - Egyptian Time Periods

WHAT WE'LL COVER

- The Old, Middle, and New Kingdoms of Egypt
- Egypt's Golden Age
- The Egyptian form of government and dynasties
- Egypt's culture and religion

YOUR ACTION ITEMS

1. Read Chapter 5, Egyptian Time Periods, and take notes in your Journal. You can also use the internet, library books, and videos to assist in your research.
2. Review the Terms & Concepts and the Historical and Mythical Figures & Places below. Also, review the Chronology of Key Historical Events for better understanding.
3. Complete the activities in this chapter.
4. Take the quiz at the end of the chapter of what you learned.
5. Supplemental resources and website links are provided in the Parent-Teacher Guide for additional reading and learning.

STUDENT AIDS

Terms & Concepts

- Deified
- Pschent
- Stepped Pyramid
- The Battle of Kadesh
- The Peace Treaty of Kadesh
- Vassal

Historical and Mythical Figures & Places

- King Amenemhat I
- Amenhotep I
- Amenhotep IV
- Cleopatra VII
- King Djedefre
- King Djoser
- Queen Hatshepsut
- City of Memphis
- King Menes
- Queen Nefertiti
- Queen Neithhotep
- Ramesses the Great
- King Sneferu
- King Tutankhamun

- City of Herakleopolis
- King Imhotep
- Valley of the Kings

Chronology of Key Historical Events

3150 BCE	King Menes (aka King Narmer) becomes first official king of Egypt.
3100 BCE	King Menes unifies Upper and Lower Egypt.
3150-2890 BCE	King Menes wife, Queen Neithhotep, takes over Egypt.
2686-2181 BCE	Egypt's "Golden Age" and the "Age of the Pyramids."
2670-2613 BC	King Djoser becomes ruler of Egypt and is a great architect.
2667-2600 BCE	King Imhotep's life and reign in Egypt.
2613-2589 BCE	Kings Sneferu's life and reign in Egypt.
2566-2558	Khufu's son, Djedefre (aka the Son of Ra), becomes ruler of Egypt.
1541-1520 BCE	King Amenhotep begins the tradition of burial in the Valley of the Kings.
1479-1458 BCE	Queen Hatshepsut becomes ruler of Egypt.
1353-1336 BCE	Amenhotep IV in power along with his queen, Nefertiti.
1336-1327 BCE	King Tutankhamun reign in Egypt.
1279-1213 BCE	King Ramesses II rules in Egypt.
1258 BCE	The Battle of Kadesh led by Ramesses the Great, and the first recorded peace treaty, The Peace Treaty of Kadesh documented between the Egyptians and the Hittites.
666 BCE	The Assyrians invade Egypt.
30 BCE	Cleopatra commits suicide, and Egypt becomes part of the Roman Empire under Octavian.

Hatshepsut

Research and find resources about Queen Hatshepsut, her rise to power, her rule as pharaoh, and her death and legacy. We've provided a helpful link in the Parent-Teacher Guide.

Present a report on what you learned to your parent or teacher. You can create a slide show or just give a verbal report. Test your presentation skills by not reading your report verbatim (word for word). Instead, take notes of the highlights of the points you want to make, and speak as if you are having a conversation with a friend.

Make sure to include the reasons she stood out as a ruler and the differences and similarities between Hatshepsut and Cleopatra.

Frontalism

Frontalism is a distinct art form used by the Egyptians to symbolize respect for the great pharaohs. Pharaohs were drawn and painted with their torsos facing frontward, but their heads and neck were drawn from the side view or their face profile. This style was very distinct from other civilization art forms. We've provided a helpful link in the Parent-Teacher Guide that shows how to create art using this technique.

Draw a picture of a pharaoh below using the frontalism technique. Keep these frontalism features in mind when you draw your pharaoh:

1. Draw only one eye shown and outlined in black.
2. Draw the shoulders and chest drawn from the frontal view.
3. Draw the arms to show action and explain what the figure is doing.
4. Draw the lower body (hips, legs, and feet) from the side profile.

Egyptian Food

Find and cook an "authentic" recipe from this civilization. Links for several recipes are in the Parent-Teacher Guide. Or you can find your own recipes that include common Egyptian ingredients.

- Lettuce
- Onions
- Celery
- Herbs
- Dates
- Figs
- Grapes
- Beef (for the rich)
- Poultry
- Grain (for flour)
- Nuts
- Seeds
- Honey
- Wheat
- Barley

Which recipe did you choose? How did it turn out? Did it taste good or not so great? Bad? Was it easy to cook or hard? Did you have difficulty finding some ingredients? Did you substitute or change the recipe in any way?

Curses on Tombs

Explore whether curses on tombs were real. We've provided a helpful link in the Parent-Teacher Guide. Read the article but do more digging on the internet or in the library.

What resources did you find? What were your findings?

King Tut Time Game

King Tutankhamun, aka King Tut, was just nine years old when he became pharaoh in 1332 B.C. Pretty impressive, right?

Grab a timer and a friend. See who can write the most words that start with one of the letters from KING TUTANKHAMUN in Nine Minutes. Each word has to be at least four letters long.

Ready, Set, Go!

Mummified Apples

Egyptians believed the Khat (the body) was essential to the survival of the Ka (the spirit). Ka could not live forever in paradise if an Egyptian's Khat was destroyed. So the Egyptians took great pains to preserve, or mummify, a person's Khat. Now let's try and experiment by making mummified apples and see how they turn out!

Instructions for this experiment are in the Parent-Teacher Guide. When your experiment is complete, answer the questions below. Make sure to keep one apple in a container that isn't treated with salt or baking soda as a control.

We think it's fun to core the apple and cut a face using a pumpkin carving knife or popsicle stick and add holes all around, but you can also use apple slices.

Do not eat the apples or mummification ingredients.

Check your apples every few days and take notes in your journal on the changes you see.

1. How long did it take to mummify the apples?

___

2. Which salt/soda mixture worked best?

___

3. How did the apples change?

___

4. Did the apples weigh the same as they did when you first started?

___

5. How do the mummified apples compare to the control apple?

___

Egyptian Numbers

The Egyptians used a decimal system for counting. The higher number is written in front of the lower number (left to right, just like ours). If there is more than one row of numbers, you read the number from top to bottom as you move left to right.

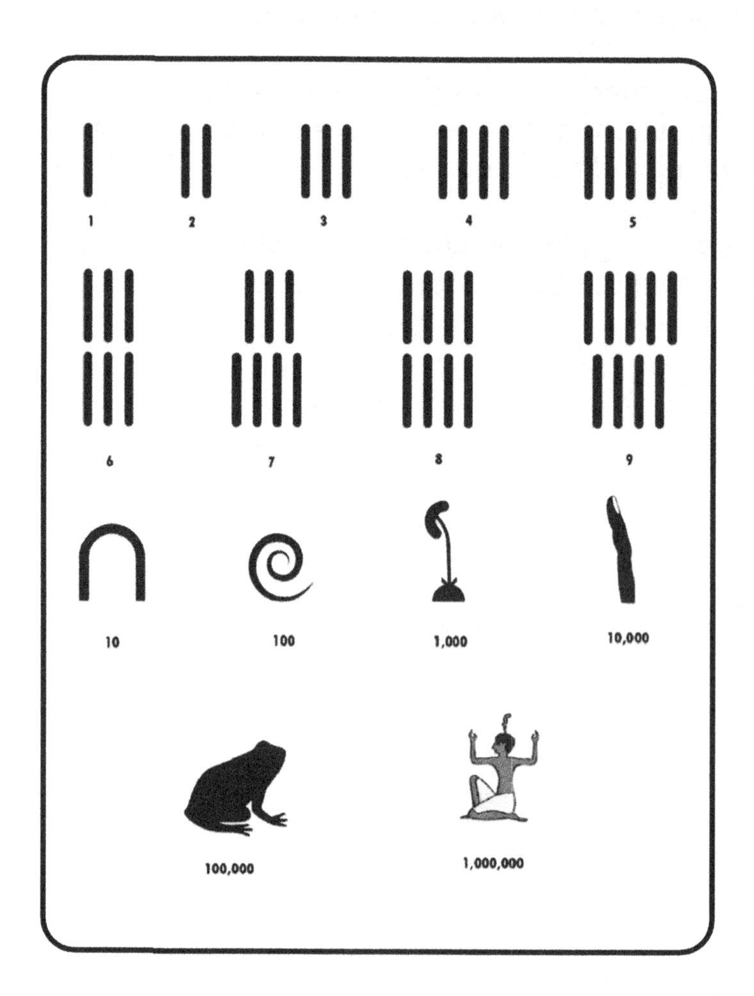

1 = a single stroke.

10 = a cattle hobble.

100 = a coil of rope.

1,000 = a water lily (lotus) plant.

10,000 = a bent finger.

100,000 = a tadpole or frog.

1,000,000 = the figure of Heh, an Egyptian deity with his arms raised above his head.

Here are a couple of examples on the next page.

2,117 (1000 + 1000 + 100 + 10 + 7)

2,112,349 (1,000,000 + 1,000,000 + 100,000 + 10,000 + 1,000 + 1,000 + 100 + 100 + 100 + 10 + 10 + 10 + 10 + 9)

Activity

1. What is the following number?

2. Write the symbols for the numbers below.

1,015

12,424

1,220,103

Copy the following paragraph, capitalize the proper nouns (a specific name for a person, place, or thing) and circle the nouns (a person, place, or thing).

Example: noun = palace, girl, book
proper noun = Buckingham Palace, Cynthia, Old Yeller

Before we get to 5000 BCE, let's rewind even further to about 15,000 years ago. This is around the Mesolithic period's beginning and just after the last ice age. At this time, nomads hunted and gathered food and supplies in the area that would later be known as Egypt. To the west, the region that is now the Sahara Desert was a savannah. Here, people lived a more settled lifestyle, grazing their herds on the open grasslands. But around 5000 BCE, a climate shift caused the Sahara region to dry out quickly. So these people moved east to the Nile River Valley, where they formed a different way of life, becoming farmers instead of herders.

Word Scramble

Unscramble the words below (hint: the terms are in the reading book and glossary)

1 DSTERE ____________________

2 NNIUBA ____________________

3 EPTYG ____________________

4 CTASDIYN ____________________

5 ENMSE ____________________

6 HAASRA ____________________

7 MSPIMHE ____________________

8 TMABAAS ____________________

9 DNIKOMG ____________________

10 IEDEIDF ____________________

11 MPIYDAR ____________________

12 EXTT ____________________

13 NYRAACH ____________________

14 LEEDAIIZD ____________________

15 RISELAM ____________________

16 RETLCUU ____________________

17 EHEYRS ____________________

18 TTRYEA ____________________

19 LSSAAV ____________________

20 PHHOARA ____________________

Time to Relax & Color

Scrapbook

Create a scrapbook, vision board, poster board, or online board like Pinterest to showcase your favorite topics that resonated with you in this chapter. Create your board with online images, or if you're creating a physical board, use images from magazines, words or phrases, or pictures you draw and color and display them on your board. Then at the end of this workbook, combine them into a single board and save your collection.

Chapter 5 Quiz

1. Why were people living in the grasslands of the Sahara Desert forced to change from herders to farmers and move to the Nile River around 5000 BCE?

2. What is a pschent?

3. Who was the first official king of a unified Upper and Lower Egypt?

4. Who was the first female ruler of Egypt?

5. Where was Egypt's first capital located?

6. What was Egypt's first significant period of prosperity, and how did they refer to it?

8. How many pyramids did Sneferu build in the cities of Meidum and Dahshur?

9. Who was the first female pharaoh to rule with all of the authority of a male pharaoh?

10. Who was known for her great beauty and the loving family she shared with King Akhenaten?

11. King Tut is recognized around the world for what?

12. Why was Ramesses II given the nickname, Ramses the Great?

13. What was the significance of the Battle of Kadesh between the Egyptians and the Hittites?

14. After Alexander the Great's death, what happened to the land he had conquered, particularly Egypt?

15. Who was the last ruler of Egypt?

16. What happened to the Egyptians in the end?

Chapter 6 - Other Mediterranean Civilizations

WHAT WE'LL COVER

- The Minoans of Crete
- King Minos and the palace at Knossos
- The Mycenaeans and ancient Greek culture
- Mycenaean religion and written language
- The Phoenicians
- Alexander the Great

YOUR ACTION ITEMS

1. Read Chapter 6, Other Mediterranean Civilizations, and take notes in your Journal. You can also use the internet, library books, and videos to assist in your research.
2. Review the Terms & Concepts and the Historical and Mythical Figures & Places below. Also, review the Area Map and Chronology of Key Historical Events for better understanding.
3. Complete the activities in this chapter.
4. Take the quiz at the end of the chapter of what you learned.
5. Supplemental resources and website links are provided in the Parent-Teacher Guide for additional reading and learning.

STUDENT AIDS

Terms & Concepts

- The Trojan War
- Linear B
- The Greek Dark Age
- Linear A
- The Amarna Letters
- The Punic Wars

Historical and Mythical Figures & Places

- Alexander the Great
- Athens
- Byblos
- The Dorians
- Hercules
- Homer
- King Minos
- The Palace at Knossos
- Poseidon
- Zeus and Europa

Area Map

Chronology of Key Historical Events

7000-6000 BCE	People arrive on the island of Crete from Asia Minor.
4000 BCE	The Phoenicians establish the city of Sidon.
3000 BCE	The Phoenician city of Byblos is founded by their god, El.
2000 BCE	The Minoans become prosperous through trade.
1900-1100 BCE	The Mycenaeans appear in mainland Greece.
1500-332 BCE	The Phoenicians become mega-traders, colonizers, and manufacturing giants.
1450 BCE	The Mycenaeans become the dominant civilization in the Aegean.
1230-1100 BCE	The Dorians invade the Mycenaeans.
600 BCE	The Minoan civilization reaches its peak.
333 BCE	Alexander the Great arrives in Phoenicia.

Authentic Mediterranean Recipes

Find and cook an ancient Mediterranean recipe. Links for several recipes are in the Parent-Teacher Guide. Or you can find your own recipes that include common Mediterranean ingredients.

- Lentils
- Chickpeas
- Beans
- Sheep
- Rabbit
- Cattle
- Chicken

- Cereal
- Pomegranates
- Figs
- dates
- Apples
- Almonds
- Limes

- Grapes
- Quinces
- Olives
- Cheese
- Honey
- Eggs

Which recipe did you choose? How did it turn out? Did it taste good or not so great? Bad? Was it easy to cook or hard? Did you have difficulty finding some ingredients? Did you substitute or change the recipe in any way?

Time to Relax & Color

The Tyrians

In the book, we covered Alexander the Great's military campaigns, particularly his conquest of the Tyrians. You'll recall that the cities of Sidon and Byblos had acknowledged Alexander's greatness with many gifts, and as a result, Alexander had left these two cities intact. The city of Tyre thought they would do the same thing and sent an envoy to meet Alexander along the way with gifts just as lovely as those Sidon sent. Alexander accepted them, and everything looked good so far. However, a siege escalated, and for five months, the two sides fought, with Alexander slewing 8,000 Tyrians and selling 30,000 more into slavery. What do you think Alexander the Great's motivations were? If you were the Tyrians, what decision would you have made (not considering the outcome) and why? Write your answers in the space provided below.

The Minoans

About 7000 to 6000 BCE, a dark-haired group of people arrived on the island of Crete from Asia Minor, known as the Minoans. They are sometimes called Cretans after their island home. Read about the Minoans in Chapter 6 or do your own research and answer the questions below.

1. How did the Minoans come to exist?

2. What made the Minoans unique?

3. What contributions did the Minoans leave for future civilizations?

4. What happened to the Minoans in the end?

The Mycenaeans

The story of the Mycenaeans is like the prologue to the story of the ancient Greeks. The Mycenaean culture will contribute a lot to the Greeks who come later. And the Greeks will, in turn, influence art, science, literature, philosophy, and so much more around the world. Read about the Mycenaeans in Chapter 6 or do your own research and answer the questions below.

1. How did the Mycenaeans come to exist?

2. What made the Mycenaeans unique?

3. What contributions did the Mycenaeans leave for future civilizations?

4. What happened to the Mycenaeans in the end?

The Phoenicians

Phoenicians were brave, seafaring traders who dominated the Mediterranean and connected the known world with their complex system of trading routes. They were also manufacturers and innovators. Some of their products were so prized that many larger civilizations left them alone simply so that they would not disrupt the supply of goods that the Phoenicians made. Read about the Phoenicians in Chapter 6 or do your own research and answer the questions below.

1. How did the Phoenicians come to exist?

2. What made the Phoenicians unique?

3. What contributions did the Phoenicians leave for future civilizations?

4. What happened to the Phoenicians in the end?

"Tyrian" Purple Tie Dye (sort of)

As we highlighted in the book, the Phoenicians were known for their purple-dyed goods, so we thought it would be fun for you to create your own "Tyrian" purple tie dye toga (or shirt) using permanent markers! The instructions for this activity are in the Parent-Teacher Guide.

How did it turn out?

What did you like or dislike about it?

Was it messy? Would you make it again?

Paste a picture of your creation below.

Grammar & Stories

Choose 25 words for the following parts of speech below.

Five Nouns:

Five Compound Words:

Five Adjectives:

Five Verbs:

Five Proper Nouns:

Write a story, play, song, or poem using the words from your list. Your theme is the Minoan life. Read, recite, or sing your masterpiece to your family or friends.

The Minoan Double Axe

The double axe was an important sacred symbol of the Minoan religion in ancient Crete. Some say it symbolized the creation of the Mater-arche or ancient Greek origins and that it only accompanied female goddesses and never male gods. A link for a video on The Minoan Double Axe is in the Parent-Teacher Guide. Watch the video, or another video of your choice, to learn more about the styles, uses, and symbolism of the Minoan Double Axe, and answer the questions below.

1. Double axes for everyday use were made of what material? ______________________

2. ______________________________ were used for religious ceremonies.

3. Some ceremonial axes were made of gold, true or false? ______________________

4. ______________________________ is one possible reason for using gold.

5 It is believed the double axe is the most sacred symbol of a solar goddess, true or false?

____

Below, draw and color two samples of Minoan axes, one for everyday use and one for ceremonies.

Word Search

Circle the words from the list below. The words may be placed horizontally (forward or backward), vertically (up or down), or diagonally.

```
S T C E J B O E V I T O V M I N O A N S
J D D Y L J J M Y D J V V M T D L K Z M
N D W D P X G J Q T T T T Z B J N P P M
Y K N Y N P D X R Y J L R L N A E N T M
S R E T T E L A N R A M A B I A J W V L
U X S M J D Y D M H W P L C R R B W B M
C B R E L K L W C T R P I O M V B R G Y
O J I M I R T R O J A N H O R S E R L M
M P M Q J R A R L L E P M T H Y A B N T
M G I Q U I A A R O M Y R E V V P R P J
O K N G R I B S H A C L R L E P C M Q G
D Y K T M Y T P S E S C M C J R T M J M
I L A R R E D O N I U E I N E M E X M D
T M Q I T O N A U L M R O T T G N P P P
Y B N Z R G E T E S C E A C A D Q T Y Y
T T K I T A L S N L B N Z R S D L P Q B
H J A L N J T Z E X S X O B D E E K N D
N N L J G Y J S R P B N Z G D J R L K K
S K R T Y J Y Y G X S R L Z Q R R F S Z
```

MINOANS	CRETANS	LABYRINTH	VOTIVE OBJECTS
COMMODITY	FRESCOES	AMPHORAE	UBIQUITOUS
PIGMENT	MATRIARCHAL	MYCENAEAN	TROJAN HORSE
CITADELS	HERCULES	MEGARONS	EMISSARIES
GRAVE CIRCLES	DORIANS	PHOENICIAN	AMARNA LETTERS

Scrapbook

Create a scrapbook, vision board, poster board, or online board like Pinterest to showcase your favorite topics that resonated with you in this chapter. Create your board with online images, or if you're creating a physical board, use images from magazines, words or phrases, or pictures you draw and color and display them on your board. Then at the end of this workbook, combine them into a single board and save your collection.

Chapter 6 Quiz

1. The King immortalized in Homer's epic poem, *The Odyssey*, was____________________ .

2.____________________ is the name of the largest Greek Aegean island.

3. The Minoans used a form of writing called____________________ .

4. The Mycenaeans modified the Minoan form of writing to create

____ .

5. The Minoans had distinctive artistic styles and were famous for their

____ .

6. A tall pottery jar with two vertical handles used primarily to transport and store olive oil, wine, and other foods is called an____________________ .

7. Whose religion was primarily led by women, worshipping goddesses who oversaw animals, crops, and the home?____________________ .

8. The most famous palace on Crete was ____________________ .

9. The island of Thera is now modern-day____________________

10.____________________ are Mycenaean-fortified cities and settlements.

11. The factors that caused the decline and collapse of the Mycenaeans include:

a. ____

b. ____

c. ____

d. ____

12. The Mycenaeans created palace complexes around central courtyards called ______________

______________________________.

13. The Mycenaeans are seen as the beginning of ______________________________________.

14. The Mycenaeans constructed what kind of tombs at their burial sites?

______________________________.

15. The Mycenaeans were invaded and conquered by the ______________________________.

16. __________________________ were seafaring traders who dominated the Mediterranean, connecting the known world with their complex system of trading routes, and conducting their transit trade.

17. ____ was the most influential colony in North Africa.

18. In 332 BCE, mainland Phoenicia was conquered by the Greeks, led by __________________

_______________________.

19. ____ created our modern-day alphabet.

20. Who ruled the Phoenicians after Alexander the Great?________________________________

Chapter 7 - The Greeks

WHAT WE'LL COVER

- The Greeks on the Mediterranean and the Aegean seas
- The Greek pantheon and acropolis
- The ancient Olympic Games
- The famous city-states of Sparta and Athens
- Greek contributions to western society
- The Greco-Persian War, The Peloponnesian War, and Roman conquerors

YOUR ACTION ITEMS

1. Read Chapter 7, The Greeks, and take notes in your Journal. You can also use the internet, library books, and videos to assist in your research.
2. Review the Terms & Concepts and the Historical and Mythical Figures & Places below. Also, review the Area Map and Chronology of Key Historical Events for better understanding.
3. Complete the activities in this chapter.
4. Take the quiz at the end of the chapter of what you learned.
5. Supplemental resources and website links are provided in the Parent-Teacher Guide for additional reading and learning.

STUDENT AIDS

Terms & Concepts

- Hellenistic
- Philosophy
- The Battle of Thermopylae
- The Socratic method
- The Pythagorean Theorem
- Acropolis
- The First Peloponnesian War
- The Second Peloponnesian War
- The Olympic Games
- Architectural orders
- Chiton
- The Trojan War
- The Persian Wars
- First and Second Macedonian Wars
- Battle of Actium

Historical and Mythical Figures & Places

- Mount Olympus
- Olympia
- Socrates
- Plato
- Aristotle
- King Phillip II
- Hippocrates
- Plutarch
- Homer
- Euripides
- Herodotus
- The Macedonians
- Alexander the Great
- Solon
- Xerxes I
- Archimedes

Area Map

Chronology of Key Historical Events

1300-1200 BCE	The Trojan War between Greek city-states and the city of Troy.
1200 BCE	The collapse of the Mycenaeans.
776 BCE	The Olympics held every four years.
750 BCE	Homer writes the Iliad and the Odyssey.
640–560 BCE	Solon (aka the Founding Father of Athens) comes to power replacing Draconian laws and setting the stage for democracy.
585 BCE	Thales, sometimes called the First Philosopher, inquires into the origins of the universe.

571-497 BCE	The life of the philosopher and mathematician Pythagoras.
559 BCE	Cyrus II (aka Cyrus the Great) rises to power.
470/469-399 BCE	The life of Socrates (aka The Father of Western Philosophy).
484-425/413 BCE	The life of Herodotus the Father of History.
484-407 BCE	The life of Greek playwright, Euripides
480 BCE	City of Athens destroyed by the Persians.
480 BCE	Xerxes I invades the Greeks in the Battle of Thermopylae.
479 BCE	Persia defeated by Greeks.
460-446 BCE	The First Peloponnesian War.
443 BCE	Pericles elected to Athenian general.
447-432 BCE	The Parthenon on the Acropolis constructed.
431-404 BCE	The Second Peloponnesian War.
430 BCE	The plague hits Greece killing 100,000 people.
428-347 BCE	The life of Philosopher Plato.
384-322 BCE	The life of Philosopher Aristotle.
359-338 BCE	King Philip II takes the Macedon throne and conquers Greece.
338 BCE	Philip and Alexander the Great defeat Athens and Thebes.
300 BCE	The life of the mathematician, Euclid.
287-212 BCE	The life of Archimedes (aka The Father of Mathematics).
214-205 BCE	The First Macedonian War.
200-197 BCE	The Second Macedonian War.
31/30 BCE	The Romans conquer Greece taking over Alexander’s empire.
45/50-120/125 CE	The life of Plutarch

Greek Mythology

We learned in Greek Mythology about the Olympian god and goddesses that lived on Mt. Olympus. There were heroes, too, like Hercules, who was half god, half human. The heroes helped the Greeks relate even more closely to the gods since they were half mortal like themselves. There were also the Titans, a whole other family of gods and goddesses who preceded the Olympians. Then, there were all of the monsters. These were not always scary, gross creatures as we think of monsters today. Instead, they were any mythological beast, like Pegasus, the winged horse, or the one-eyed Cyclops credited with building the enormous cyclopean walls. Invent a mythological creature and write a story about it.

The Olympics

Research and write a report on one aspect of modern Olympics that interests you.

We've provided a few helpful links to get you started in the Parent-Teacher Guide.

It could be a specific sporting event or a tradition, such as the lighting of the Olympic torch, or a symbol, such as the Olympic rings. How has this aspect changed since the ancient Olympics and the event's history or tradition?

Time to Relax & Color

Cooking Greek Cuisine

Who doesn't Love Greek cuisine? And ancient Greek cuisine is not unlike the Mediterranean foods we see today. Visit the links in the Parent-Teacher Guide and choose one of the recipes to make, or find your own authentic Greek recipe and make it.

1. Which recipe did you choose?

____

____

____

2. Was the recipe easy or difficult to make and why?

____

____

3. Did you enjoy eating the food you made?

____

____

4. Did you make any substitutions? If so, what were they?

____

____

5. Would you make the recipe again?

____

____

6. Did you share the meal? If so, with whom and did they like it?

____

____

The Greek Chiton

Make your own Greek Chiton (pronounced Kīton).

A link that shows you how to make a chiton is in the Parent-Teacher Guide.

Materials:

- small white sheet or large white t-shirt
- two safety pins
- ribbon or cord

Present your Debate in the next activity while wearing your Chiton. Have a picture taken of you wearing your chiton and paste it below:

Debate

Write and present a speech (oration) persuading a family member or teacher that it would be better to live in Athens rather than in Sparta.

Now, switch sides and convince them Sparta would be better.

Socrates

Socrates wanted people to question what they believed and why they believed it. So he would start with a simple question and continue to question based on each response. This way of going back and forth, each answer leading to more questions, came to be called the Socratic method.

1. Accompany your parents or guardians on a trip to the store.
2. Play the role of Socrates and dress the part. Don't forget to wear your chiton.
3. As your parents/guardians choose items in the store, ask them questions about their choices.

   Your questions should follow in line with each answer, but here are a few to consider:

   a. Why did you choose that particular item?
   b. Do you feel this item is superior to other items?
   c. Did color, weight, and packaging affect your decision?
   d. Did you consider the price, and if so, why?

4. Track your questions and answers below.

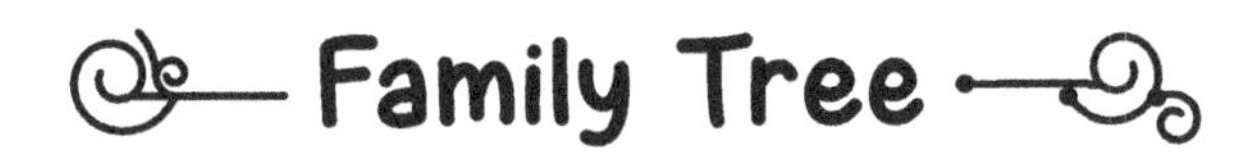

Family Tree

Trace your family history and design a family tree. As you learned in the book, the Greek pantheon consisted of twelve major gods and goddesses called Olympians because they were said to live on sacred Mount Olympus. There were many other gods and goddesses in this family tree besides those that resided on Mount Olympus. Hades, brother of Zeus and god of the underworld, is just one example. Watch the video; the link is provided in the Parent-Teacher Guide, and list the names of the 12 gods of Olympus.

Next to each name, draw a picture of a symbol that represents what they ruled over.

How to Create Your Family Tree.

Gather information about your family(ies) by asking family members for help. Pictures and original documents can be useful to prepare your family tree. If your family lineage is unknown, make a family tree of the Olympians.

1. Write down the details as you gather the information. Preparing an outline can be helpful here.
2. A link to a site for free family tree templates is provided in the Parent-Teacher Guide. Choose or design the model you want to create using one of the free templates researched or draw one free-hand. It can be as simple as writing the family tree out with pen and paper or using a poster board with markers.
3. Once completed, share your family tree diagram with family and friends.

Copywork

Copy the following paragraph and circle the adjectives (a word that describes the traits, qualities, or a number of a noun. A noun can also be an adjective if it describes another noun).

Example: a **happy** dog
A **home** office

Pottery is one of the most useful and common artifacts for an archeologist to learn about a particular society. It was available in ample supply, not valued by treasure hunters, and durable even when broken. Pottery styles also changed over time, making it possible to accurately date archeological findings based on pottery fragments. Greek pottery is no exception and displays this civilization's artistic and practical talents. Amphorae for wine and olive oil were very common, as well as other jugs, pitchers, drinking cups, and plates. Most vessels for liquids feature vertical handles, a narrow neck, and some kind of foot or base. A three-handled hydra for water was another everyday piece.

Word Match

Review the terms and definitions below and match the number on the left to the definition on the right.

1 Norms	______	early Greek philosophers who would travel from city to city and, for a fee, tutor the sons of private citizens and give lectures
2 Helot	______	a legendary animal combining features of animal and human form or having the forms of various animals in combination, as a centaur, griffin, or sphinx
3 Archipelago	______	the Greek's personification of victory
4 Pantheon	______	a Spartan slave
5 Hero	______	based on experiments or experience rather than ideas or theories
6 Monster	______	conversations around a particular theme
7 Oracle	______	the fact of words containing sounds similar to the noises they describe, for example, hiss
8 Odes	______	a behavior pattern or trait considered typical of a particular social group
9 Olympiad	______	the attribution of human nature or character to animals, inanimate objects, or abstract notions, especially as a rhetorical figure

10 Nike	____________	a person who is admired by many people for doing something brave or good
11 Personification	____________	a machine that pumped water out of the hulls of ships
12 Philosophy	____________	a four-year period between the Olympic Games
13 Empirical	____________	a system of government in which the people of a country can vote to elect their representatives
14 Sophists	____________	a large group or chain of islands
15 Impiety	____________	a mathematical equation developed by Pythagoras
16 Dialogues	____________	an utterance, often ambiguous or obscure, given by a priest or priestess at a shrine as the response of a god to an inquiry; the agency or medium giving such responses
17 Onomatopoeia	____________	a poem
18 Archimedes Screw	____________	the study of the nature and meaning of the universe and of human life
19 Pythagorean Theorem	____________	lack of respect for the gods
20 Democracy	____________	the ensemble of a culture's religious figures

Scrapbook

Create a scrapbook, vision board, poster board, or online board like Pinterest to showcase your favorite topics that resonated with you in this chapter. Create your board with online images, or if you're creating a physical board, use images from magazines, words or phrases, or pictures you draw and color and display them on your board. Then at the end of this workbook, combine them into a single board and save your collection.

Chapter 7 Quiz

1. How did the Greeks come to exist?

2. What made the Greeks unique?

3. What contributions did the Greeks leave for future civilizations?

4. What happened to the Greeks in the end?

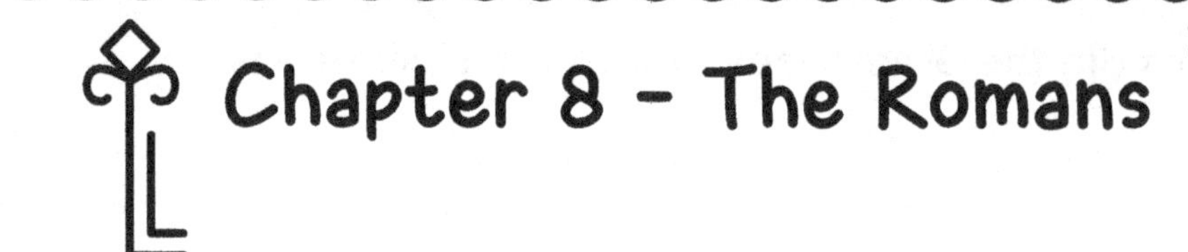

Chapter 8 - The Romans

WHAT WE'LL COVER

- The city of Rome's founding
- Roman adaptation of Greek culture
- The Roman Republic
- Roman contributions to society
- The Roman Empire
- Julius Caesar and Emperor Constantine
- The decline and fall of Rome

YOUR ACTION ITEMS

1. Read Chapter 8, The Romans, and take notes in your Journal. You can also use the internet, library books, and videos to assist in your research.
2. Review the Terms & Concepts and the Historical and Mythical Figures & Places below. Also, review the Area Map and Chronology of Key Historical Events for better understanding.
3. Complete the activities in this chapter.
4. Take the quiz at the end of the chapter of what you learned.
5. Supplemental resources and website links are provided in the Parent-Teacher Guide for additional reading and learning.

STUDENT AIDS

Terms & Concepts

- Battle Of Milvian Bridge
- Council Of Nicaea
- Gladiator
- Spectacles
- The Edict Of Milan
- The First Triumvirat
- Ides Of March
- Tetrarchy Or "Rule Of Four."

Historical and Mythical Figures & Places

- Julius Caesar
- Mark Antony
- Nero
- Emperor Constantine I
- The Roman Forum
- Octavian (Augustus)
- Mt. Vesuvius & Pompeii
- Constantinople

Area Map

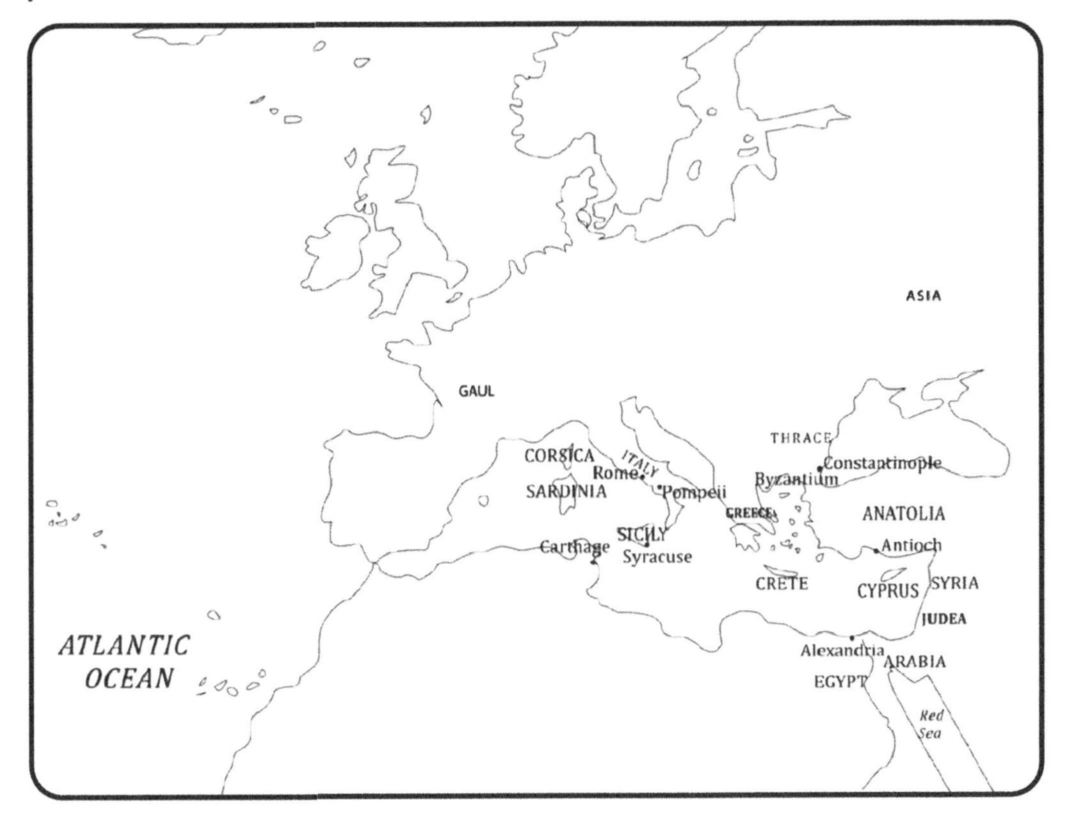

Chronology of Key Historical Events

753 BCE	The City of Rome is founded by Emperor Romulus.
700 BCE	The rise of Rome.
534–510 BCE	The reign of Rome’s last king, Tarquin the Proud.
509 BCE	Tarquin overthrown, and the Roman republic begins.
390 BCE	The Gauls sack and burn the city of Rome.
264-261 BCE	The First Punic War for control of Sicily.
247–183 BCE	The life of Hannibal.
218-201 BCE	The Second Punic War for control of Rome.
149-146 BCE	The Third Punic War.
146 BCE	Rome annexes the entire Greek peninsula.

106-43 BCE	The Life of Marcus Tullius Cicero.
100-44 BCE	The Life of Julius Caesar.
73-71 BCE	Spartacus and his army destroy the Italian countryside pursued by Roman armies.
66 BCE-14 CE	The life of Caesar's adopted nephew Gaius Octavius Thurinus (Octavia)
60 BCE	Caesar forms the First Triumvirate alliance (Gang of Three) with Gnaeus Pompeius Magnus (Pompey the Great) and Marcus Licinius Crassus.
59 BCE	Caesar invades Gaul, The First Triumvirate breaks up, Crassus killed in battle, and Julia dies in childbirth, breaking Pompey's family bond with Caesar.
49 BCE	49 BCE take over Pompey's control of Rome.
44 BCE	The assassination of Julius Caesar (The Ides of March).
44 BCE	Octavian comes to power in Rome.
43 BCE	Octavian forms the Second Triumvirate alliance with Mark Antony and Marcus Aemilius Lepidus avenging Caesar's death.
33 BCE	Bathhouses in Rome appear.

Marketing

The ancient Roman road network stretched for over 75,000 miles. Mile markers along the way showed the distance to the next town and gave travelers other important information, like the best places to stop. As time went on, more information was added, and the mile markers became bigger, some even up to six feet tall!

You work in the marketing department of your company. You have been tasked to create a business ad to add to a mile marker. First, you need to create a service or product for ancient Rome. Then you need to create an ad for it. The person seeing the ad must understand your product or service quickly, and it needs to be brief because you have limited space.

What is your service or product?

Write your ad here:

Roman Emperors

Choose a Roman Emperor and do some research. Helpful links are provided in the Parent-Teacher guide. Write a report about this emperor and include the following: Who were his relations? How did he rise to power? Was he cruel, kind, both? Did the people he ruled support him? Did he have a positive impact on Rome, and in what way? How did his leadership end?

Toga Time

The iconic toga was a draped outer garment that the ancient Romans wore. It was initially thought to have been worn by both males, females, and the citizen-military. However, gradually women adopted a type of clothing called a stola, and togas became more recognized as formal wear for male Roman citizens and the distinctive garment of the upper classes.

Togas were worn over a tunic. The togas were made from white wool and draped over the shoulders and around the body. Color and pattern were rigidly prescribed for most wearers. For example, senators and candidates wore white togas (toga candida); freeborn boys, until puberty, wore a purple-bordered toga; after reaching puberty, adolescents began to wear the plain man's toga; people in mourning wore dark colors; and for triumphs and, in the later period, as worn by consuls, the toga was richly embroidered and patterned.

Wrap yourself correctly in a toga or stola. We've provided some helpful links in the Parent-Teacher Guide.

Draw a self-portrait of you in the toga or stola below.

Time to Relax & Color

Cooking in Rome

The ancient Romans loved to eat frittatas, which is kind of like an omelet (and so do we!). They have eggs, vegetables, meat, and cheese. Frittatas can be eaten for breakfast, lunch, or dinner. After the first meal, we love to eat leftover frittata cold, stuffed into a buttered roll. Yum!

We've provided a link to some of our favorite frittata recipes in the Parent-Teacher Guide, or you can use your own family's recipe if you have one.

Make a delicious meal for your family. Serve with a side salad, and if you want, you can top a slice of frittata with a dollop of sour cream or crème fraiche and a sprinkling of fresh herbs.

Do some research and find other ancient Roman dishes and list them here. Look up the history behind baked dormice. The dish was originally made from a dormouse. What? Mice? Now we just use chicken!

Create A Newspaper For Ancient Rome

Create a newspaper for your Roman readers! This is a great way to assimilate what it was like living in ancient Rome. You'll play all of the different roles in developing your newspaper, such as the Editor, the Reporter, the Printer, and the Photographer. Or you can do this as a group, so grab your friends! Be creative with your newspaper. Online newspaper software programs can aid in the design and layout, or you can use an online app or even draw and color your newspaper on paper and piece it together.

It's important to understand the various elements and different sections of a newspaper so that you'll have an idea of what to include as content. Newspapers are all about written articles, so as the Editor, you will design and layout your newspaper around those articles, including different sections of the newspaper like Politics, the Editorials, the Classifieds, Sports & Entertainment, etc. Be sure to plan how much room each section of your newspaper will take as space is limited, but a good goal is to aim for two to three articles per page.

As a Reporter, you must accomplish the job within assigned space limits, and each of your articles shouldn't be more than 500 words long. A good rule to follow is to have a piece of paper for each article you plan to write about and make sure it's typewritten and in a column format like this paragraph. As the Photographer, you should have 1-2 corresponding photographs per article. It's always easy to resize the images than it is to resize the articles.

As the Printer, it's your job to insert all of the articles and images and get them situated and aligned well. You don't want your newspaper to look too crowded! Crop pictures to fit the space you have and shrink and stretch them to keep everything proportional. You also don't want to use too many font styles. A good guide is to use 11pt or 12pt font for the body or copy text, and 14pt or 16pt font size for article titles. The largest text should be the newspaper name itself.

Leave the same amount of space between the articles, text boxes, and images you have between columns, and try and keep at least 1/8th of an inch between all columns. Remember, consistency is key!

Build a Roman Road Model

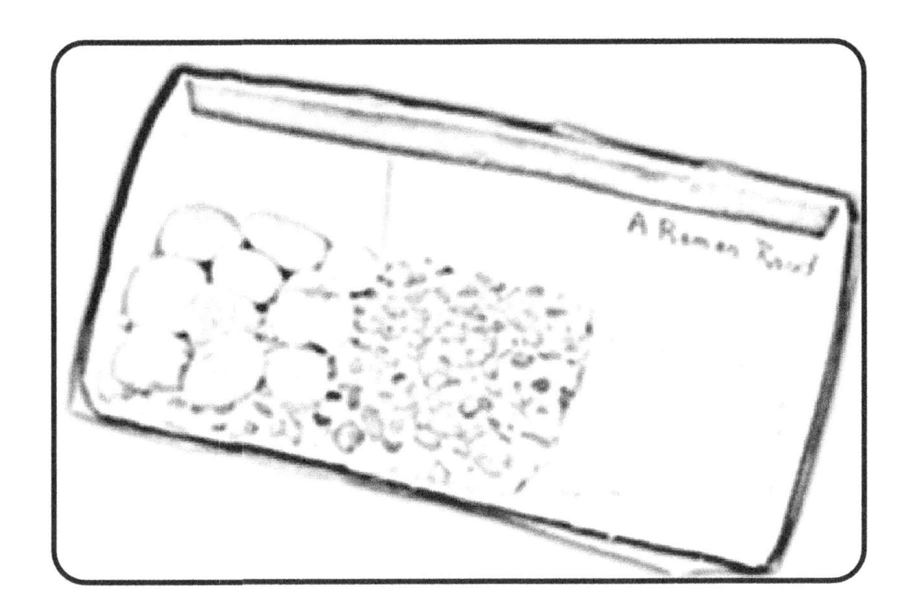

Collect these materials and prepare your project work surface:

1. Shoe Box
2. Glue
3. Clay
4. Gravel
5. Spoon
6. Smooth Stones
7. Container for mixing

The instructions for this activity are in the Parent-Teacher Guide. Take a picture of the final product and paste it below.

Timeline Matchup

Match the number on the left with the correct time period on the right.

1- 753 BCE	______________	The Republican Period
2- 753-508 BCE	______________	Gauls raided Italy
3- 509-27 BCE	______________	City of Rome Founded
4- 509 BCE	______________	Second Punic War
5- 27 BCE - 476 CE	______________	Octavian - 1st Emperor
6- 390 BCE	______________	First Punic War
7- 264-261 BCE	______________	The First Triumvirate
8- 218-201 BCE	______________	The Imperial Period
9- 60 BCE	______________	Ides of March
10- 44 BCE	______________	The Regal Period
11- 27 BCE	______________	End of the Roman Empire
12- 476 CE	______________	Rome formed a Republic

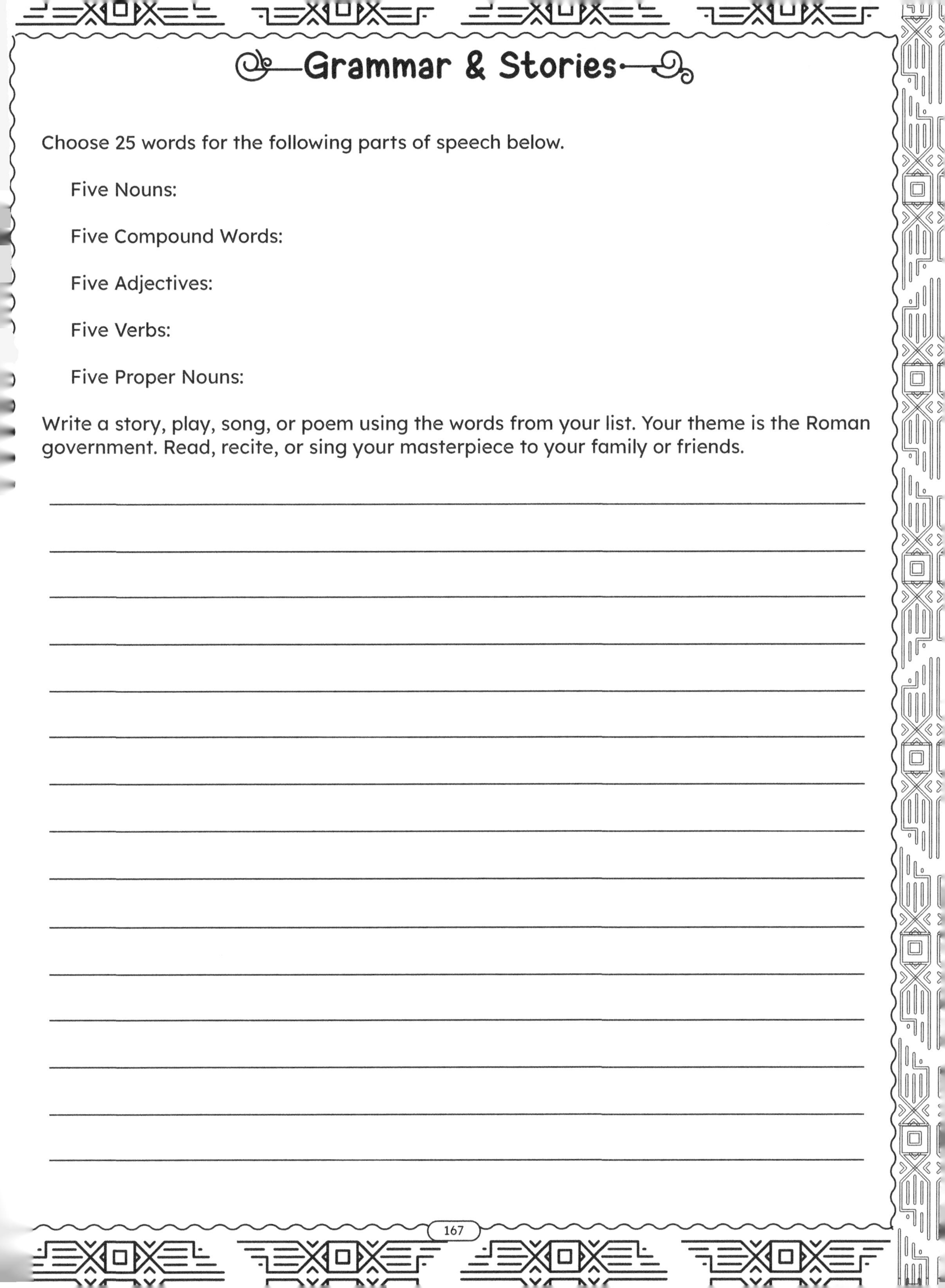

Grammar & Stories

Choose 25 words for the following parts of speech below.

Five Nouns:

Five Compound Words:

Five Adjectives:

Five Verbs:

Five Proper Nouns:

Write a story, play, song, or poem using the words from your list. Your theme is the Roman government. Read, recite, or sing your masterpiece to your family or friends.

Word Scramble

Unscramble the words below (hint: the terms are in the reading book and glossary)

1 ITYAL ______________________

2 USRLOMU ______________________

3 LNSTAI ______________________

4 ASCTSRNUE ______________________

5 COENRSAT ______________________

6 WSPHIOR ______________________

7 ASMK ______________________

8 RILPIEMA ______________________

9 TXONIEFP ______________________

10 SEAVLT ______________________

11 NIARTAPIC ______________________

12 LONCCIFT ______________________

13 NRSCIOIRENTU ______________________

14 GORADLTAI ______________________

15 STSEPLCAEC ______________________

16 ARRYTM ______________________

17 RCSIUC ______________________

18 MEUSOOLSC ______________________

19 DGUSLAI ______________________

20 TAASREGMTI ______________________

Roman Numerals

Roman numerals are combinations of letters used in place of numbers as seen in the chart below.

Roman Numeral	Amount	Roman Numeral	Amount
I	1	C	100
V	5	D	500
X	10	M	1,000
L	50		

Review the links in the Parent-Teacher Guide and watch one or more of the videos on Roman numerals, and then answer the questions below.

1. What alphabet do Roman numerals come from? ____________________

2. What number is missing from the Roman numeral system? ____________________

3. How many of the same numeral can you use in a row? ____________________

4. To subtract a number, does the smaller number go before or after a larger number?

____

5. To add a number, does the smaller number go before or after a larger number?

____

6. How do you write 1,243? ____________________

7. What number is MMDCXXVIII? ____________________

Scrapbook

Create a scrapbook, vision board, poster board, or online board like Pinterest to showcase your favorite topics that resonated with you in this chapter. Create your board with online images, or if you're creating a physical board, use images from magazines, words or phrases, or pictures you draw and color and display them on your board. Then at the end of this workbook, combine them into a single board and save your collection.

Chapter 8 Quiz

1. How did the Romans come to exist?

2. What made the Romans unique?

4. What happened to the Romans in the end?

3. What contributions did the Romans leave for future civilizations?

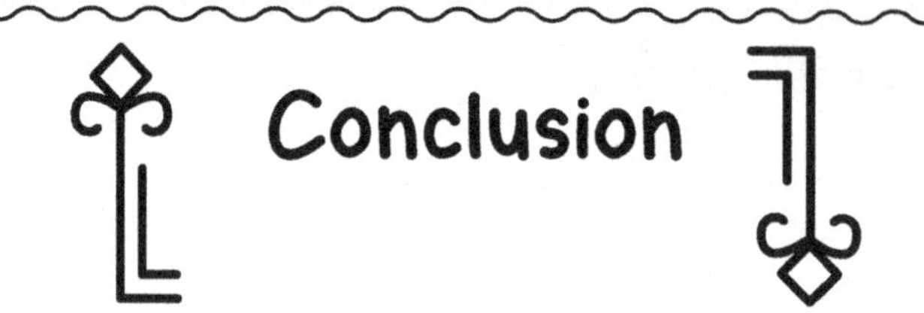

Conclusion

WHAT WE'LL COVER

- How more informed we are about the world around us and how it came to be
- How we can foresee where our civilization might be headed
- What you found personally inspiring
- An appreciation for diversity
- Telling your story

YOUR ACTION ITEMS

1. Read the Conclusion and take notes in your journal. If you used the internet, library books, or videos to assist in your research, then review your findings.
2. Complete the activities in this chapter.
3. Complete the Conclusion Questions of What You Have Learned.
4. Supplemental resources and website links are provided in the Parent-Teacher Guide for additional reading and learning.

Civilization Favorites

Make a list of the civilizations we learned about below. If you could go back in time, which civilization would you want to live in? Answer that question below and why you chose that civilization to live in.

Compare and Contrast

Pick one of the characteristics of a civilization that most interested you:

- Art
- Religion
- Conflict, Wars, Battles
- Architecture
- Government & Politics
- Agriculture
- Inventions

Write a report below choosing two civilizations and compare and contrast your chosen characteristic.

Make Your Own Lyre

Lyres are musical instruments played by the ancient Greeks and Romans. The Roman emperor Nero fancied himself a musical prodigy and—rather than working on the problems of Rome—preferred to spend all his time singing (badly) and playing the lyre.

Collect these materials and prepare your project work surface to make your own lyre:

1. Pencils for tracing
2. Markers or Crayons
3. Stapler
4. Scissors
5. 2 pencils for your lyre model
6. 4-7 rubber bands of various sizes
7. Template of the lyre (found in instructions)
8. A cardboard box that is at least 9 inches long on one side and 2.5 inches high on th other side

The instructions for this activity are in the Parent-Teacher Guide. Take a picture of the final product and paste it below.

Ancient Religions

Religion played a vital role in ancient society, and every ancient culture had different beliefs, gods, goddesses, and ways of worship. Religion, then as now, gave people a way of making sense of their world. Religion could explain things people didn't understand: day and night, seasons, storms, comets, or diseases. It also provided a comforting sense of control over the unknown. Choose two ancient religions that existed in early times and write a comparison below. How are they the same? How are they different?

World Waterways

Explore how rivers, oceans, and water were essential to the rise of many cultures. Compare the past to the present day and discuss how rivers, oceans, and water are used today in the space below.

Forms of Currency

Look up the modern-day civilizations for each ancient civilization covered in the book: Mesopotamia, Egypt, Greece, Rome, and other Mediterranean Civilizations, and list them below. Look up exchange rates and list the currency and the exchange rates for the equivalent of one US dollar. Helpful links have been provided in the Parent-Teacher Guide.

Country Mesopotamia (list countries below)	Currency (i.e. Dinar)	Exchange Rate 1 USD
1.__________	__________	1 USD = __________
2.__________	__________	1 USD = __________
3.__________	__________	1 USD = __________
4.__________	__________	1 USD = __________
5.__________	__________	1 USD = __________
Egypt	Egyptian pound	1 USD = __________
Greece	__________	1 USD = __________
Rome	__________	1 USD = __________
Other Mediterranean Minoan (list country below)		
1.__________	__________	1 USD = __________
Mycenaean (list country below)		
1.__________	__________	1 USD = __________
Phoenician (list countries below)		
1__________	__________	1 USD = __________
2__________	__________	1 USD = __________
3__________	__________	1 USD = __________

Draw a picture of a single unit of each country's primary form of currency. For example, one US dollar.

Forms of Government

Define the terms below and identify one or more ancient civilizations for each of the listed governing forms.

1. Democracy

   a. Definition:

   ____

   ____

   b. Which civilizations have this form of government?

   ____

   ____

2. Monarchy

   a. Definition:

   ____

   ____

   b. Which civilizations have this form of government?

   ____

   ____

3. Tyranny

   a. Definition:

   ____

   ____

b. Which civilizations have this form of government?

4. Oligarchy

a. Definition:

b. Which civilizations have this form of government?

What's Different?

Find the 8 differences in the pictures below, then add your own artistic touches to the illustrations and color.

Scrapbook

Take your scrapbook, vision board, poster board, or online board from each chapter and combine them into a single board, and save your collection. Take a picture and paste it below.

Conclusion Questions of What You Have Learned

1. Which of the technologies from ancient civilizations you studied do you personally use the most today and in what way?

2. Who was your favorite person we learned about, and how have they inspired you?

3. If you could meet that person, what would you ask them? What would you tell them about yourself?

4. Are there any elements of rise or decline that you see in the world around you today?

4. Which civilization most surprised you with its advanced technology, knowledge, and sophistication?

5. Do you have a greater appreciation of what it means to vote and have a public voice?

Wow, Piper! That was such a fun adventure, learning so much about ancient civilizations that established who we are as humans and gave us an understanding of where we came from. Yes, Pavi, it sure was!! Thank you everyone for joining us!! But it's time for Piper and me to go and head off to our next adventure. It sure is, Pavi, and I can't wait. See you next time, everyone!

We know many families have more than one student working on the activities. We are providing a pdf copy of this workbook, so you can make copies of the pages. Just use the QR code below to get access to the download. Please play fair. Only make copies for your family. Thank you!

Made in the USA
Las Vegas, NV
17 September 2023